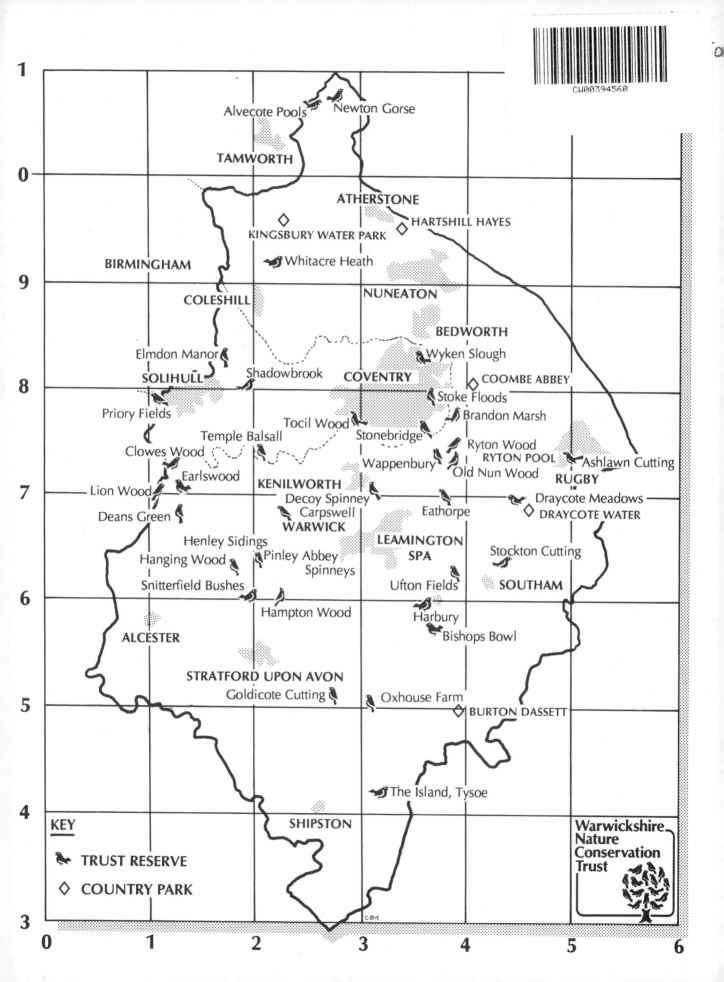

The Nature of Warwickshire 1990
has been published
in a Limited Edition
of which this is

Number 80

A list of subscribers
is printed at the
back of the book

THE NATURE OF WARWICKSHIRE

OVER: Warwickshire west of Henley-in-Arden. (CM)

THE NATURE OF WARWICKSHIRE

THE WILDLIFE AND NATURAL HISTORY
OF WARWICKSHIRE, COVENTRY AND SOLIHULL

Edited by
DR ANDY TASKER

with written contributions from George & Maurice Arnold, Juliet Bailey,
Joe Hardman, Graham Harrison, David Morfitt, John Roberts, Professor Fred
Shotton, Roger Smith, Chris Thomas, and Adam Wright

published in association with
WARWICKSHIRE NATURE CONSERVATION TRUST

and with the support of
THE ROYAL SOCIETY FOR NATURE CONSERVATION

BARRACUDA BOOKS LIMITED
BUCKINGHAM, ENGLAND
MCMLXXXX

PUBLISHED BY BARRACUDA BOOKS LIMITED
BUCKINGHAM, ENGLAND
AND PRINTED BY
SOUTHAMPTON BOOK COMPANY
SOUTHAMPTON ENGLAND

BOUND BY
GREEN STREET BINDERY
OXFORD, ENGLAND

JACKET PRINTED BY
CHENEY & SONS LIMITED
BANBURY, OXON

COLOUR PRINTED BY
RAVEN PRINT, OXON

COLOUR LITHOGRAPHY BY
SOUTH MIDLANDS LITHOPLATES LIMITED
LUTON, ENGLAND

LITHOGRAPHY BY
FORE COLOUR GRAPHICS LIMITED
HERTFORD, ENGLAND

TYPESET BY
HARPER PHOTOTYPESETTERS LIMITED
NORTHAMPTON, ENGLAND

ISBN 0 86023 473 8

Contents

Acknowledgements

A book of this type obviously depends on the skills and goodwill of many people, and I would like to take this opportunity to thank them all for their help.

The authors of the book, with their main areas of contribution, were: George & Maurice Arnold (North Warwickshire); Juliet Bailey (farming); Joe Hardman (South Warwickshire); Graham Harrison (birds); Dave Morfitt (land use history); John Roberts (wild flowers); Professor Fred Shotton (geology); Roger Smith (butterflies & moths); Chris Thomas (urban wildlife) and Adam Wright (invertebrates and reptiles). I have already apologised to them for altering almost all their words in an attempt to produce a coherent and readable style throughout the text. All the errors and omissions are mine, but I hope they are few.

In addition, many other people added their specialist knowledge of wildlife groups or parts of the county, so augmenting different parts of the book. They include: Nigel Bailey, Chris Brooke-Harris, Pam Copson, John Crossling, Stan Finch, Ron Hill, Paul Holley, Edwin Hopkins, Steve Lane, David Marriott, Phil Parr Keith Warmington and Neil Wyatt.

Organising and obtaining the photographs has taken a huge amount of time, quietly and efficiently undertaken by Colin Marsay, who also converted many of the colour slides into the black-and-white prints required for the plates. The photographers, with their initials as used on each plate, were: Ray Allen (RA), Gus Ariss (GA), Juliet Bailey (JAB), John Ball (JB), Tris Besterman (TPB), Den Cooper (DRC), Rod Courtman (RC), Tony Dyke (ARD), Mick Finnemore (MWF), Tony Hamblin (TH), Janet & Graham Harrison (JV&GRH), Brian Keates (BSK), Mike Lane, (ML), Jeff Lewis (JWK), Colin Marsay (CM), Frank Millington (FCM), Alan Millward (AGM), Steve Plant (SP), Kay Reeve (KR), John Roberts (JRR), Jim Russell (JSR), Fred Shotton (FS), Andy Tasker (AT), Chris Thomas (CMT), Margaret Thorne (MST), Adrian Wallen (ACW), Keith Warmington (KW), Adam Wright (AW) and Neil Wyatt (NMW). In addition to thanking them for the photographs that we have used I would also like to thank them all for so generously offering hundreds of other pictures that we have been unable to include. Editing such good pictures has certainly not been easy!

The figures and drawings illustrating the text were coordinated and collated by Chris Brooke-Harris. Illustrators' initials, as given with each drawing, were: Steve Alton (SDA), Chris Brooke-Harris (CBH), Heather Colman (HC), Pam Copson (PJC), John Crossling (JC), Michael Goodrum (MG), Margaret Jones (MJ), Amanda Maddocks (AM), Mark Mason (MM), Dave Morfitt (DRM), Antonia Phillips (AP), Martyn Laidlow (ML), Dave Shuker (DS), Fred Shotton (FS), Andy Tasker (AT) and Jeremy Wyatt (JPW).

We are also grateful to the following for their kind permission to reproduce these photographs: Academic Press (AP), British Museum Natural History (BMNH), Coventry Evening Telegraph (CET), Warwickshire Museum (WM), Warwickshire Record Office (WRO).

For a few photographs and drawings in the Trust library it has not been possible to trace the originator, so the general Trust credit (WNCT) has been used, with our apologies.

Finally, thanks are also due to Rachel Wells and Annette Hughes who typed various drafts of the text, to Ruth Moffatt who helped by obtaining copyright clearance for some of the diagrams, to Brian Hewetson who produced the index, to Pam Copson, Lesley Davies, Duncan Jeffray, Roger Smith and Chris Thomas who proof-read the text. I would like to add my own thanks to all the staff and trainees at Warwickshire Nature Conservation Trust for helping to complete the project on time, and to my family for putting up with it all.

I hope our joint efforts make Warwickshire's wildlife that much more appreciated.

8

Foreword

by Sir David Attenborough

I grew up in the Midlands of England and I can well remember the joys and excitement of finding out, first hand, about natural history. One of my first forays was into geology. What were these strange fossils? How did they get into the rocks? Of what long-ago animals and plants were they part?

This fascination with finding out about the wild led me into a study of living animals and plants; then my work in television as a producer enabled me to travel the world looking at its wildlife and wild places. The spectacular tropical rainforests of Borneo, the bleak wilds of Alaska, the arid deserts of Namibia: all have their own wild animals and plants, adapted in intricate and intimate ways to their own environment.

These international travels served to remind me, more forcibly than I ever learned in textbooks, that all the species of the world depend on each other, and that we in turn depend on them. Without the diversity of plant and animal life the world simply would not work. It is not just a question of us telling the rest of the world what they should do, either; we must do something here in Britain too. The first step is to find out just what is still here.

And so I welcome this book, which brings together a host of experts to tell the story of Warwickshire, from its rocks and history to the woods, meadows and rivers of today. Over the centuries people have had a massive impact on wildlife, yet even in Warwickshire fragments still remain of tremendous importance and stunning beauty. We must treasure these last wildlife sites and protect them for the future, not just for our own enjoyment, but to show the rest of the world that there is a future for wildlife. I hope you will find the book both interesting and informative, as well as an encouragement for you to conserve Warwickshire's wildlife heritage.

Dave Attenborough

Dedication

Dedicated to the memory of
Professor Fred W. Shotton
(1906-1990).

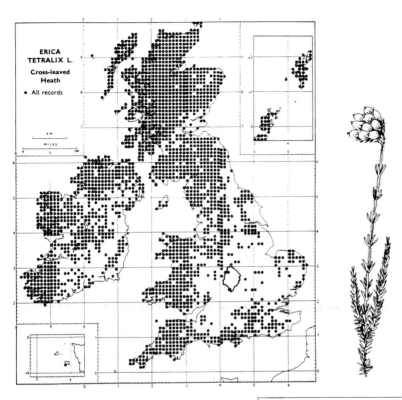

Cross-leaved heath and dipper are mainly found on moorlands or in upland Britain, just reaching the north and west of Warwickshire. (For credits see p.13.)

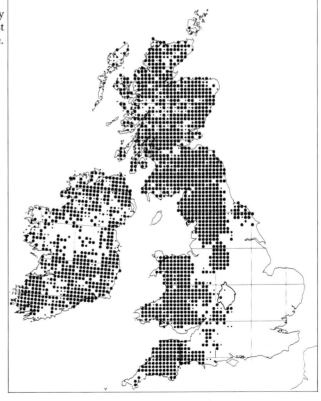

10

Introduction

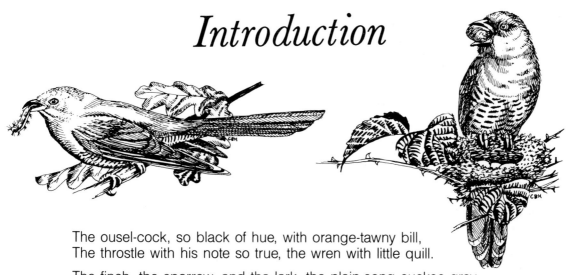

The ousel-cock, so black of hue, with orange-tawny bill,
The throstle with his note so true, the wren with little quill.

The finch, the sparrow, and the lark, the plain-song cuckoo gray,
Whose note full many a man doth mark, and dares not answer nay

A Midsummer Night's Dream

The nature of Warwickshire has been influenced by many factors over the last few thousand years: its climate, geology, soils and its people have all had significant impacts. Over the last hundred years people have changed the shape of the county, and more or less everything growing and living within it. With the urbanisation of Birmingham and Coventry, the growth of towns from Nuneaton to Shipston, and the intensively used farmland of the rest of the county, at first sight there is very little nature left. However, this book aims to show that wildlife and natural places still flourish in Warwickshire if you know where to look. All of Shakespeare's birds have survived the last 400 years and are still flourishing today, although the ousel has changed its name to a blackbird.

The county itself lies at the very heart of England, at the watershed of two great river systems: the River Tame flowing north and east into the Trent and then the North Sea, and the River Avon flowing south-west towards the Severn and the Irish Sea. This major watershed is remarkably difficult to see on the ground, as the gently rolling landscape gives few clues. Indeed, gentle hills and valleys are typical of most of the county, with nearly all of the land between 50 and 150 metres (160-500 feet). Higher ground occurs in the north, in a ridge from Nuneaton north-west through Hartshill to Grendon, although even its highest point does not quite reach 180 metres (600 feet). Towards the south and east, higher ground occurs along the Oxfordshire border at Edge Hill but the highest point in the county straddles the Gloucestershire border near Ilmington, where Ebrington Hill reaches 259 metres (850 feet).

This position at the centre of England, with low-lying ground, makes the climate generally moderate. South-westerly gales have blown themselves out by the time they get to Warwickshire and northerly blasts have lost some of their impact, yet the clouds still bring sufficient rain to keep the fields green. Average rainfall is slightly greater on the higher ground of the Birmingham Plateau at Solihull, and the higher ground west of Nuneaton, with drier areas along the Avon valley encouraging crop irrigation. Frosts are sometimes more noticeable in the Midlands than nearer the coast, causing some problems to fruit growers. The summer temperatures may also be a degree or two warmer than at the coasts, yet there are no noticeable changes for plants or animals.

Warwickshire's geographical position means that some plants and animals of upland Britain just reach the county in its north and west edges. Birds like the dipper, needing fast-flowing streams, and bell heather, a plant of the upland moorlands, are two good examples. In contrast, some plants and animals of the warmer south-east, with its chalky soils, manage to squeeze into the southernmost parts of the county. The nightingale, dependent on coppice woodland, and the clustered bellflower, a plant of lime-rich grassland, just make it over the border. Still other species, like midland hawthorn, have a stronghold in the county.

The boundaries of Warwickshire were changed significantly when the new county of West Midlands was established in 1974, taking Coventry and Solihull with it. For this book we have considered Warwickshire to include both Solihull and Coventry, as this is the area covered by Warwickshire Nature Conservation Trust. On the ground this area totals over 550,000 acres (225,000 hectares), with just over one million inhabitants: close to two people for every acre. The 'old' county of Warwickshire also included land at Tamworth, and much of the eastern part of Birmingham, as well as the famous Sutton Park. Given the importance of the park for heathland, we have included this in the book too. National biological recording is also carried out using a version of this 'old' county boundary, referred to as Vice-County 38.

Ask for the most famous woodland in Warwickshire and many will reply 'the Forest of Arden'. However, it seems likely that this name was first used long after most of the original wildwood had been cleared, and when most of the area had little woodland. Despite many of the remaining woods being converted to conifer plantations, remnants of ancient broadleaved woodlands dating back for at least four centuries still persist today, providing an invaluable habitat for wildlife as well as a link with the past. Trees were much more widespread in the countryside up to fifty years ago, when 'leafy Warwickshire' was a truly descriptive phrase. However, the ravages of Dutch elm disease and modern farming methods have both had their impact, altering both the landscape and its wildlife value.

Heathland, once so widespread and reflected in so many district names, is now almost gone. In the small areas where it survives, its characteristic wildlife continues to thrive. The meadows of Shakespeare's time occupied perhaps half the county, with a rich mixture of wild flowers and insects. Now most have been replaced by intensive agriculture but small fields still remain to remind us of the beauty of our wild flower heritage.

While many habitats have been destroyed, others have been created, including important lakes and wetlands in areas of old mining and quarrying. Towns too have become increasingly important for wildlife, as have the canals, railway embankments and road verges which link them together.

This book aims to be an introduction to those factors making Warwickshire what it is today. It begins with a chapter providing a summary of the geological past, before examining the last two thousand years in more detail. The main habitats of the county, and the plants and animals that depend on them, form the basis of the next four chapters. The way people have influenced the nature of Warwickshire by farming and by development are next outlined in two chapters while the final chapter looks at the future for wildlife within this densely populated area.

All the placenames and names of animals and plants referred to in the text are indexed, allowing locations to be found and species identified. Some sites are Trust nature reserves, where conservation management is the first concern, but many others are in private ownership with no public access. As there are over 10,000 different species of animals, plants and fungi recorded from the county it has not been our intention to include all of them: instead we have tended to pick on those species most readily identified, including wild flowers, butterflies, birds and mammals. Metric measures are used throughout except for areas, which are given in acres (not hectares) as most people seem to understand the former better. A conversion of 2.47 acres to the hectare may be useful if you prefer the metric equivalent.

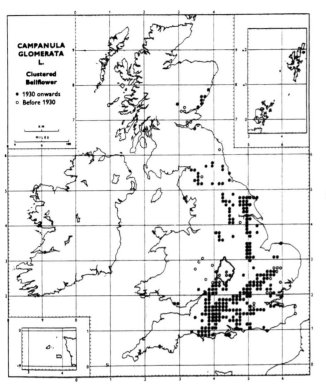

Clustered bell-flower and nightingale mainly occur in the south-east of England, just reaching Warwickshire. (Drawings CBH except dipper JPW: plant distribution maps by kind permission of BSBI and EP Publishing; bird distribution maps by kind permission of BTO and T&AD Poyser)

Given the book's size and scope it cannot provide all the answers to all the questions about the nature of Warwickshire, but we hope it provides a good breadth of information as well as a stimulus to find out more. We have borrowed from Warwickshire's most famous author for our chapter bylines, as Shakespeare's use of nature in his plays gives some valuable insights into the county of 1600. As we near the year 2000, we can see some of the effects of 400 years of expanding population on our natural world.

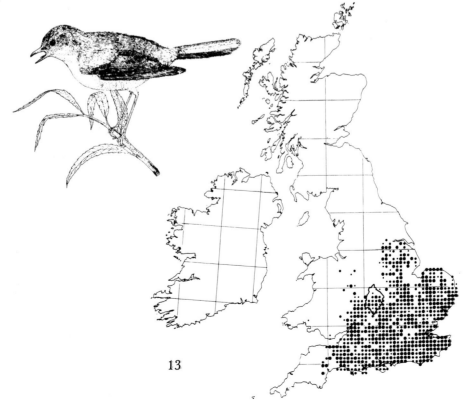

13

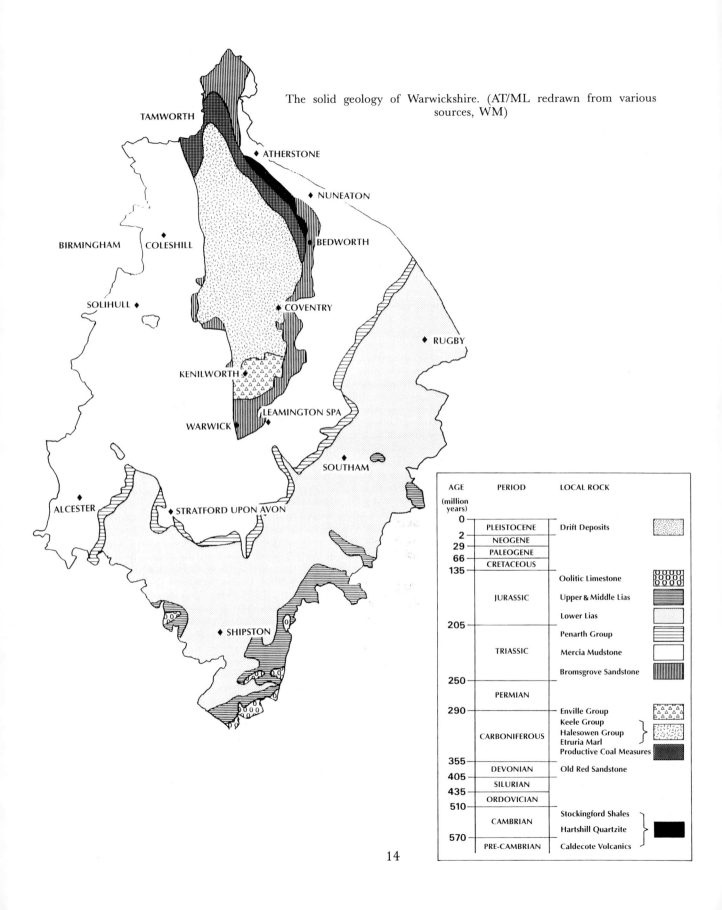

The solid geology of Warwickshire. (AT/ML redrawn from various sources, WM)

AGE (million years)	PERIOD	LOCAL ROCK	
0	PLEISTOCENE	Drift Deposits	
2	NEOGENE		
29	PALEOGENE		
66	CRETACEOUS		
135	JURASSIC	Oolitic Limestone	
		Upper & Middle Lias	
		Lower Lias	
205	TRIASSIC	Penarth Group	
		Mercia Mudstone	
		Bromsgrove Sandstone	
250	PERMIAN		
290	CARBONIFEROUS	Enville Group	
		Keele Group Halesowen Group Etruria Marl	
		Productive Coal Measures	
355	DEVONIAN	Old Red Sandstone	
405	SILURIAN		
435	ORDOVICIAN		
510	CAMBRIAN	Stockingford Shales Hartshill Quartzite	
570	PRE-CAMBRIAN	Caldecote Volcanics	

14

On the Rocks

Antres vast and deserts idle
Rough quarries, rocks and hills whose heads touch heaven

Othello: The Moor of Venice

The nature of Warwickshire today is based on its past. Evidence from the last thousand million years is stored in the rocks that make up the county, giving glimpses of tremendous variations in climate and water levels over that vast period. At times Shakespeare's 'deserts idle' would have been an excellent description of the county; at other times the hills must have been tall enough to 'touch heaven'; there may even have been times when there were huge caves (or 'antres') too. Besides forming the character of Warwickshire today, the rocks have been used by generations of people for housing, fuel and industry.

Rocks can be formed in one of two ways. Sedimentary rocks were produced from broken-down pieces of other rocks, laid down as sands, silts or clays beneath rivers, lakes or oceans, or even blown by the wind over deserts. They may have been transported for a long distance before reaching their present positions. Limestones are also formed as sediments, laid down directly on the sea floor by temperature-controlled chemical reactions. Igneous rocks, in contrast, occur where hot molten rock is injected from deep within the earth's core into points of weakness in the rock surface. They may form volcanoes, forcing ash and larva over wide distances, or they may cool and solidify before reaching the surface. The intense heat and pressure associated with these igneous rocks can also transform nearby sedimentary rocks, altering both their chemical and physical composition, so creating 'metamorphic' rocks.

As sediments fall on ocean floors, they form distinct layers. Over periods of hundreds of thousands of years new layers build on top of the old, producing a precise time sequence. Trapped within these sediments are the remains of creatures that lived at that particular moment and, although the soft parts of their bodies usually rot away, any hard materials remain. Bones, teeth, and shells are obvious examples, but much more than these can be preserved in the right conditions, forming fossils. As the pressure of overlying sediments builds up, so the original substance may be changed by a process called mineralisation, to form an exact replica of the object, made from calcium carbonate or silica. Sometimes only a mould is left of the external or internal shape of the object. Very occasionally, fossils are formed where even the soft parts of the animal or plant are preserved, giving minutely detailed pictures of these ancient organisms.

Over long periods of time the surface of the earth changes too, with ocean floors raised up as mountains and land sinking into the seas. When weather acts on the mountains, erosion occurs, bringing new sediments down into rivers and seas. This erosion also exposes old sediments, forming outcrops of rocks of different ages. Dating all these rocks is possible, using the natural rates of breakdown of certain chemicals, and relative ages can be deduced from the fossils present. Together these enable an entire sequence of different ages to be built up, each given different names from the 'Pre-Cambrian' of over six hundred million years ago up to the 'Pleistocene' of the last two million years.

In Warwickshire, the oldest rocks are the Pre-Cambrian 'Caldecote Volcanic Formation', outcropping near Nuneaton. These earliest remains point to a volcanic landscape of ash and lava. The Cambrian period of 550 million years ago is represented by a prominent ridge, running north-west from Nuneaton towards Atherstone. Here the rocks dip steeply into the ground, leaving exposed a 280 metre thickness of Hartshill Quartzite under 900 metres of Stockingford Shale. The quartzite is made up of layers of silica sand, cemented together to form a hard rock: in places igneous rocks known as diorite have been squeezed into the quartzite, giving thin sheets or 'sills'. Quartzite, diorite and Pre-Cambrian volcanic rocks are quarried at Man-Abell's Quarry near Nuneaton, and further up the ridge a wider sill of diorite forms the main supply quarried at Mancetter. In between are many other quarries at Oldbury, Hartshill and Camp Hill, where the hard rocks are excavated for use primarily as roadstone and aggregates in concrete. At Mancetter the heat produced by the sill's formation resulted in a spectacular growth of crystals of the mineral pyrite, or fool's gold.

Just to the north of Hartshill itself, Woodlands Quarry has provided some of the oldest fossils in the country. These were found in a red limestone within the quartzite, and include various fragments of shells and tubes such as *Kutorgina*, a primitive brachiopod shellfish; *Coleoloides*, the oldest fossil shell in Britain and *Hyolithus*, a conical shell. The limestone is known as the Hyolithes limestone after the latter animal, and the entire quarry is now protected as a Site of Special Scientific Interest (SSSI).

The Stockingford Shales were formed from the sands and muds of a deep ocean. They encompass virtually the whole of Cambrian time and have been penetrated by many boreholes in the search for concealed coalfields. Fossils here are rare, but some trilobites have been discovered; these marine animals superficially resemble modern woodlice, but they had a huge armoured head shield and many flexible body plates, allowing the animal to roll up. Also found here are the earliest graptolites – branched thread-like organisms producing buds of unknown function. Later volcanic activity forced molten rock into these shales, producing a hard rock called spessartite, quarried at Griff near Bedworth.

The end of the Cambrian era in Warwickshire was marked by the rising seabed, forming dry land which persisted for nearly 100 million years. The next rocks present in Warwickshire were laid down at the end of the Devonian, about 370 million years ago, when coarse sandstones were formed near what is now Mancetter.

Other than a small area of Millstone Grit near Dosthill, the next major rock-forming activity occurred in the Carboniferous period, about 300 million years ago, when a huge delta swamp extended from Russia to Ireland, crossing north Warwickshire. Trees such as giant horsetails, club-mosses and seed-ferns grew prolifically in the moist sub-tropical climate. Periodically the large rivers feeding these deltas flooded, burying the vegetation in sands and silts. New forests then grew, only to be buried in turn, so forming the repeating sequences of sandstones and coal seams that comprise the Productive Coal Measures. From time to time the sea invaded the low-lying deltas, depositing bands of grey shale containing fossils of marine species such as the bivalve mollusc *Dunbarella* and the brachiopod shellfish *Lingula*. Fossils of trees that formed the coal itself include *Calamites*, a giant horsetail; *Lepidodendron*, a giant club-moss; and *Neuropteris*,

CENTRE: Cross Hands Quarry near Long Compton (JRR) BELOW: Reconstruction of the unique amphibian fossil Dasyceps from the Permian at Kenilworth. ABOVE LEFT: Examining the boundary between the red Mercia Mudstone, grey 'tea green marl', and darker mudstones and shales of the Penarth Group: Round Hill Road, Wootton Wawen. (TPB/WM) CENTRE: Fossilised tooth of an elephant (*Elephas primigenius*) from the Permian at Wasperton (FWS) and fossil head of *Ichthyosaurus intermedius* from the Lower Lias at Binton. (TPB/WM) RIGHT: Fossilised stem of a seed-fern (*Sphenopteris*) from the Carboniferous at Bedworth. (FWS)

17

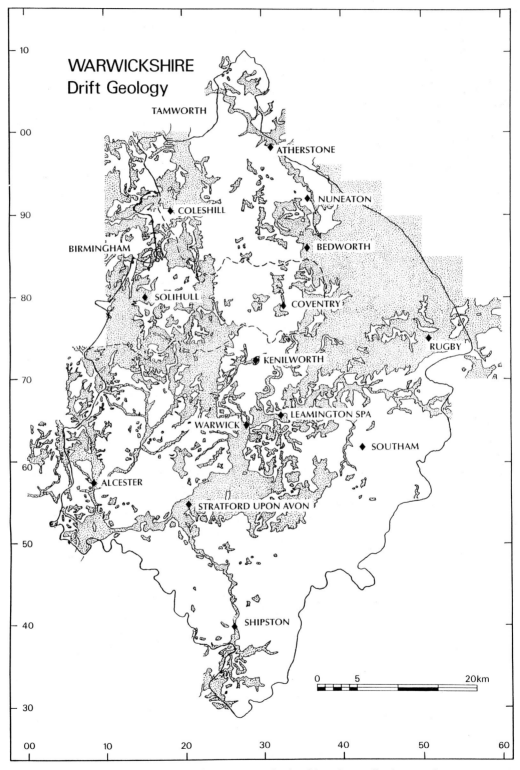

WARWICKSHIRE
Drift Geology

TAMWORTH

ATHERSTONE

NUNEATON

COLESHILL

BIRMINGHAM

BEDWORTH

SOLIHULL

COVENTRY

RUGBY

KENILWORTH

LEAMINGTON SPA

WARWICK

SOUTHAM

ALCESTER

STRATFORD UPON AVON

SHIPSTON

0   5   20km

Overlying drift deposits of sands, gravels, boulder clays, alluvium and
river terraces. These have been deposited over the last 2 million years by
both glaciers and rivers. (JC/WM)

a seed-fern. Although seed-ferns are long extinct, today horsetails survive in Warwickshire as their diminutive relatives and tiny club-mosses are found in upland Britain. The Productive Coal Measures are closest to the surface in a line from Bedworth through Nuneaton to Polesworth, becoming deeper towards the south. Mining has so far extended from Alvecote in the north of the county as far south as Coventry, but boreholes confirm deeper thin coal seams south of Leamington Spa.

Above the Productive Coal Measures, but still within the Carboniferous, are the sandstones and clays of four separate formations: Etruria Marls, Halesowen Sandstones, the Keele Group and the Enville Group. Etruria Marl is a purplish clay much used for making deep red bricks and tiles as well as the famous 'Staffordshire Blue' bricks. It contains few fossils but does include beds of pebbles, known as 'espleys', formed during ancient erosion periods. The Enville Group spans the boundary from the Carboniferous to the Permian, and among its sandstones are few fossils, except for casts of ancient conifers found at Websters brickworks SSSI in Coventry. The quarry at Longford Brickworks has now been filled in, but it contained well preserved seed-ferns.

Amphibians were around in the Permian and a unique fossil found near Kenilworth – *Dasyceps* – allows their shape and size to be studied in detail. Fossil tracks in the ancient mud have also been discovered, implying the biggest of these amphibians reached about 100cm long. Sandstones from both Carboniferous and Permian have been used for notable local buildings. The former for the old Coventry Cathedral and the latter for Kenilworth Castle. At the end of the Permian, massive earth movements caused earthquakes, changing the shape of the land as mountains were formed.

The Triassic of 250 million years ago is mainly represented in the county by Mercia Mudstone (or Keuper Marl as it used to be known) a red-brown mudstone giving colour to soils all over the centre of the county. Below and within the mudstone are various sandstones, often quarried locally for buildings including many churches, Coombe Abbey, Whitley Abbey and Warwick Castle. At the end of the Triassic, the Penarth Group (formerly the Rhaetic) is composed of more layers of mudstones overlaid by a band of the locally important White Lias limestone, exposed in abandoned quarries at Ufton and Lighthorne.

The Jurassic period is dominated in Warwickshire by the Lower Lias mudstones, forming a broad belt along the south-east side of the county from Rugby to Shipston-on-Stour, then across to Alcester. Within this grey clay material is the Blue Lias, a sequence of alternating limestones and shales, responsible for the scarp slope along much of the Lias edge. The limestone itself has been extensively quarried, originally for building materials but later for cement, producing large excavations at Rugby, Stockton, Southam, and Bishops Itchington. During quarrying a wide range of fossils has been found, inhabitants of the seas of 200 million

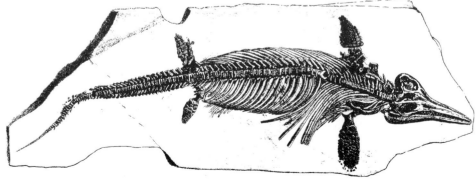

Fossils are prolific in the Lower Lias, including the famous Harbury Ichthyosaur some 10m long. (from *Fossil Reptilia of the Liassic Formations* by Owen (1861) WM)

19

years ago. These include two famous marine reptiles, *Ichthyosaurus* and *Plesiosaurus*, discovered during quarrying a hundred years ago and now in the Natural History Museum, London, with others in Warwickshire Museum. On the sea-bed were large bivalves such as *Plagiostoma gigantea* and the unequal-shelled 'Devil's toe-nail' *Gryphaea* as well as brachiopods like the ribbed *Calcirhynchia*. Swimming above them were squid-like belemnites, whose bullet-shaped 'guards' are preserved today, recognisable fish such as *Tetragonolepis* and the characteristic coiled ammonites whose shells abound in the clay. Flying above the water were dragonflies, in forms almost unchanged to this day.

Shells of the Lower Lias include (A) the 'Devils toe-nail' *Gryphaea*, (B) the giant bivalve *Plagiostoma*, and (C) brachiopods such as *Calcirhynchia*. (FS, redrawn from *British Mesozoic Fossils* (1962), BMNH)

Above the Lower Lias clays are soft clays, mudstones and ironstones of the Middle Lias, the latter giving harder cappings to hills at Burton Dassett, and forming the scarp slope at Edge Hill, where it has been extensively worked as building stone. Locally known as 'Hornton Stone', its rusty brown colour characterises many buildings in the villages of south-east Warwickshire. Above the ironstone are more soft clays of the Upper Lias and then the Inferior Oolite, typical of the Cotswolds, that just extends northwards into the southernmost parts of the county. Also quarried for building stone, the Oolitic limestone was laid down in shallow tropical seas, and contains fossils of corals among the range of different brachiopods, bivalves and sea-urchins. The shallow seas were becoming shallower, and no rocks were formed in Warwickshire from about 150 million years ago until just 2 million years ago.

Ammonites and belemnites swam in the seas of 200 million years ago.
(WM)

The Pleistocene period beginning then is marked primarily by the various Ice Ages that swept over Britain. At least the first two of these left no evidence in Warwickshire, either because the ice sheets ended too far away or because any evidence was destroyed by erosion from later glaciers. The earliest deposits are the Baginton-Lillington sands and gravels of some 450,000 years ago, laid down by rivers and streams before the advancing ice sheet. An interesting find from this period was an incomplete skull of a straight-tusked elephant, discovered in a quarry east of Snitterfield.

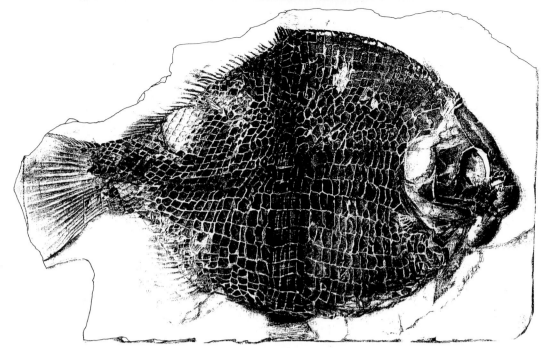

Fish included the well-preserved *Tetragonolepis*. (from *Poissons Fossiles* by Agassiz (1833) WM)

The first movements of ice over Warwickshire came from the north and north east, covering the region and indeed most of Britain, and depositing sands, clays and pebbles up to five metres thick, known as the Thrussington Till. By 400,000 years ago the ice was melting, leaving over 200,000 years of cool temperate conditions. The next Ice Age brought both ice and water to Warwickshire, with the possibility of a huge water body called Lake Harrison covering much of the Midlands at some stage. Clays laid down beneath lake water – the Wolston Clays – were later covered by Wolston Sands and Gravels deposited by rivers.

One such stream channel in a quarry at Waverley Wood contains silts with a wide range of plant and animal remains: fragments of wood, pollen, insects; a horse's tooth and even a length of elephant tusk. Mixed with the bones in the Waverley quarry was a quartzite flake with the unmistakable impact shape of a hand-struck blow: one of the first signs of people in Warwickshire.

These sands and gravels, together with the earlier deposits, and later ones too, have formed the basis for a thriving quarrying industry throughout both the Avon and the Tame valleys. The glaciers themselves, which had come from the east and north-east, deposited more clays and pebbles, this time including some limestone and chalk, and known as the Oadby Till. The deposits are mainly to the north and east of Coventry and Rugby, but traces occur elsewhere in the county. From about 125,000 to 75,000 years ago Warwickshire was sub-tropical, with evidence of hippopotamuses, lions, and people. The climate then became cold enough for mammoth and woolly rhinoceros, until about 28,000 years ago the last ice sheet came down, covering the Irish Sea and reaching eastwards as far as Wolverhampton. The conditions of icy tundra persisting over Warwickshire slowly improved from about 12,000 years ago and, despite some fluctuations, the climate became generally similar to that of today. One final effect of the ice was to lock up the planet's water, so causing sea levels to be much lower than now. Britain remained joined to continental Europe until about 7,500 years ago, allowing both plants and animals to colonise northwards, following the retreating ice.

Tetrarhynchia, a fossil brachiopod from Ironstone quarried at Edge Hill (FS, redrawn from *British Mesozoic Fossils* (1962), BMNH)

ABOVE: The oldest rocks in the county are Pre-Cambrian and Cambrian rocks, dating back over 500 million years and quarried at Judkins Quarry, Nuneaton. (WM)
CENTRE: Detail of the bedding and jointing patterns in the Cambrian shales at Merevale Lake Pits. (ARD/WM)

BELOW: The Productive Coal Measures of the Carboniferous have been exploited for centuries by mines throughout north Warwickshire as at Baddesley Pit, here in the mid-1980s. (CET)

ABOVE: Carboniferous sandstone is exposed at Corley Rocks and in this roadside cutting at Burrow Hill. (BSK) BELOW: Cherry Orchard Quarry, Kenilworth, is now a landfill site but part of the distant face of Permian Marl is to be conserved. (TPB/WM)

ABOVE: Triassic Arden Sandstone at Dinglewell Farm Quarry shows clear sedimentary layers. (ARD/WM) RIGHT: Between the Triassic Sandstones at Roundberry Quarry, Polesworth, are distinctive pebble beds. (ARD/WM) BELOW: Lower Lias limestones and shales form bands at Harbury Quarry, Bishops Itchington. Now a haven for wildlife, it is the site from which the Harbury Ichthyosaur was excavated. (JRR)

November 1928: the Harbury Ichthyosaur is discovered. It is now in the British Museum (Natural History) although others are in Warwickshire and Birmingham Museums. (WM) ABOVE: Evidence of glaciers: the 'King's Hill Erratic' carried from the east in Leicestershire and left by the melting ice at King's Hill Farm, Finham, Stoneleigh. (WM)

ABOVE: Ancient woodlands, such as Hampton Wood nature reserve on the banks of the River Avon, usually have irregular sinuous boundaries. Throughout the north and west 'Arden' half of the county, fields too are irregular and roads winding. (JB) BELOW: In contrast the 'Feldon' of south-east Warwickshire has few woods and straight hedgerows: a planned countryside. (JRR)

Out of the Past

(CBH)

The inaudible and noiseless foot of time

All's Well That Ends Well

When the last Ice Age ended around twelve thousand years ago, the ice slowly retreated northwards over Britain and during the next few thousand years, trees gradually colonised across the land bridge that then connected Britain with continental Europe. Most of Britain, including Warwickshire, became wooded – the 'wildwood' as Oliver Rackham has so evocatively called it. This natural landscape was certainly not all oak trees, as some have implied, but a complex mosaic of woodland types. The dominant tree in lowland England was in fact the now uncommon small-leaved lime – a tree still found in some Warwickshire woodlands, which may even be the managed remnants of that long-lost wildwood. Before the coming of people, the wildwood remained largely intact for thousands of years, a rich assemblage of animals and plants.

There is little direct evidence of the precise nature of the wildwood in Warwickshire, but a glimpse of what it was like comes from pollen and vegetation fragments found in river peat deposits at Shustoke in the north of the county, dating back some five to seven thousand years. There the evidence points to the wildwood containing over 80% small-leaved lime, with some large-leaved lime, rather less elm and oak, and no hazel at all. Not many miles from there the present wood at Hartshill Hayes also contains both small-leaved and large-leaved lime – a natural link stretching back at least five thousand years. Pollen evidence from Moreton Morrell in the south of the county also suggests that the wildwood there contained about 50% small-leaved lime.

From about 3000 BC Neolithic people started to clear the wildwood for farmland. Archaeological evidence for this wildwood clearance from Warwickshire is scant, but it seems likely that by the time of the Romans (from the 1st to the 5th centuries AD) at least half of the county had been cleared of its woodland. This clearance was greatest in the south-east half of Warwickshire, later known as the Feldon. Even in the heavily wooded Arden area of the north-west the evidence of Roman pottery and tile-making suggests the surviving woodlands were used for fuel, and no doubt also for building in villages and towns such as Mancetter and Alcester.

27

The Anglo-Saxon place name ending '. . .ley', meaning wood or woodland clearing, is widespread throughout the north and west, from Baddesley and Ansley through Allesley, Shirley and Hockley down to Bearley and Shrewley. This again implies that there was much woodland in this area, and that it was being actively cleared in Anglo-Saxon times. Surviving boundary charters from the period tell of woods still present today. A charter of AD704 for Shottery near Stratford-on-Avon mentions a 'Westgraf'; today Westgrove Wood is still there in Haselor. A charter of AD1001 for Long Itchington describes the bounds passing through 'a high oak in the middle of Wulluht grove' which corresponds to today's Long Itchington and Ufton Wood.

The Domesday Book in 1086 provides the first reasonably accurate picture of woodland distribution, and shows only 19% of the county was wooded. This was concentrated in the north-west, with the south-east area virtually devoid of woods. Increasing population and the consequent demand for farmland led to increasing destruction of the remaining woodland up to the period of the Black Death, when bubonic plague swept across the country in the mid-1300s. It is estimated that one third of the population was killed by the plague, so this disease was indirectly responsible for saving many of the woods which survive. Indeed, evidence from the woods themselves suggests that many expanded naturally onto unused farmland over the next few centuries, as the reduced population reorganised the villages.

There were two main types of woodland management throughout the medieval period: coppicing, where the trees were cut down on a rotational basis, and wood pasture, where domestic animals were grazed inside the wood. Even hedges separating the fields were used for wood and timber production, such was the need for woodland products.

In coppice woodlands, most of the trees – known as the 'underwood' – were cut down every 5–20 years. These cut stumps, or 'stools', then regrew naturally, producing a crop of poles of uniform size, collectively called 'wood'. This wood was mainly used for fuel but also for a wide range of domestic and agricultural purposes. Coppicing different areas of a woodland at different times gave a continuous supply of wood for local needs. Scattered among the underwood were larger trees – 'standards' – which were left to grow for several rotations of the coppice cycle before being felled to provide 'timber'. This was used for larger construction projects such as the frames of buildings or boats. The coppice-with-standards system developed over the years to become an efficient and sustainable way to produce a wide

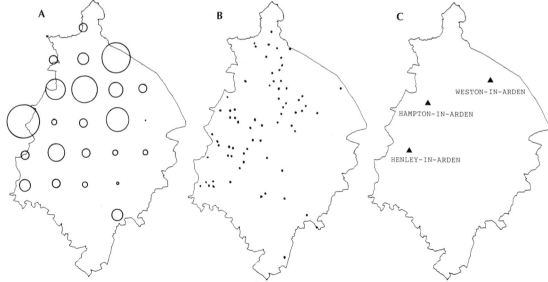

Evidence of woodland in Warwickshire – A: woodland recorded in the Domesday Book of 1086: size of circle represents the area of woodland in that 10km square, B: Saxon place name ending '. . . ley', meaning wood or wood clearing, C: Arden place names, suggesting the extent of the 'legal' Forest, but not necessarily wooded in medieval times. (A & B redrawn from the *History of the Countryside* by Rackham (1986); C: DRM)

range of woodland produce without the need for any replanting. The natural ability of most native broad-leaved trees to regrow after being felled was the simple process that kept the system going. The earliest evidence in the world for this practice of coppicing comes from wood used to make prehistoric trackways in the Somerset levels, which date back to 4000BC. By maintaining woodland at different stages of development, coppicing has created woods wonderfully rich in wildlife purely by accidental by-product. For example, nightingales are able to thrive in coppiced woods since they prefer coppice of 5–8 years' growth for nesting. The decline of the species in Warwickshire is undoubtedly related to the decline in coppicing; the same is true for dormice, now probably extinct in this county.

The only danger facing the coppice system was grazing by animals: the young shoots of coppice stools are particularly nutritious and selectively sought by both cattle and deer. Coppice woods therefore had to be protected from livestock, and an elaborate system was developed with a perimeter earth bank (the 'woodbank') surrounded by a ditch with a hedge or fence on top of the bank. The need for this woodbank is shown in records for 1403–1404,

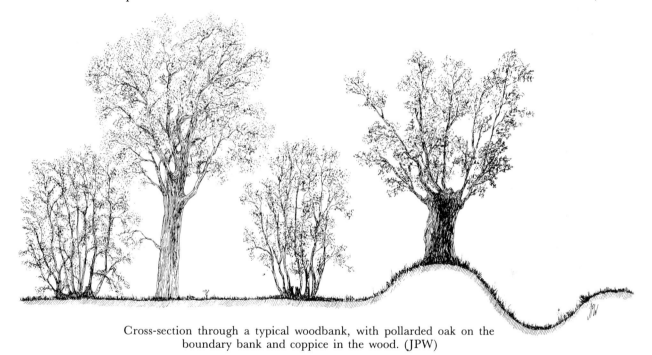

Cross-section through a typical woodbank, with pollarded oak on the boundary bank and coppice in the wood. (JPW)

where a wood which is probably now Ladbrookpark Coppice (in the Windmill Naps woodland complex) was felled and the purchaser of both wood and timber was compelled to enclose the land to ensure the next crop would not be damaged by grazing. Some woodlands from this period were managed on long rotations of 15–17 years, possibly to protect the underwood from damage by grazing, a practice carried on in Warwickshire woods until the early 1600s.

The size of the woodbank today indicates its relative age: medieval examples are usually large sinuous earthworks, about six to twelve metres across the bank and ditch, although in Warwickshire they are at the lower end of this range. In later times woodbanks were progressively smaller and straighter, so that by the nineteenth century they were little more than a small acute hedgebank. Not only did these woodbanks serve to protect the coppice from grazing damage, they also furnished permanent boundaries. Good examples of woodbanks which have survived occur at woodlands from Hartshill Hayes and Clowes Wood to Ryton

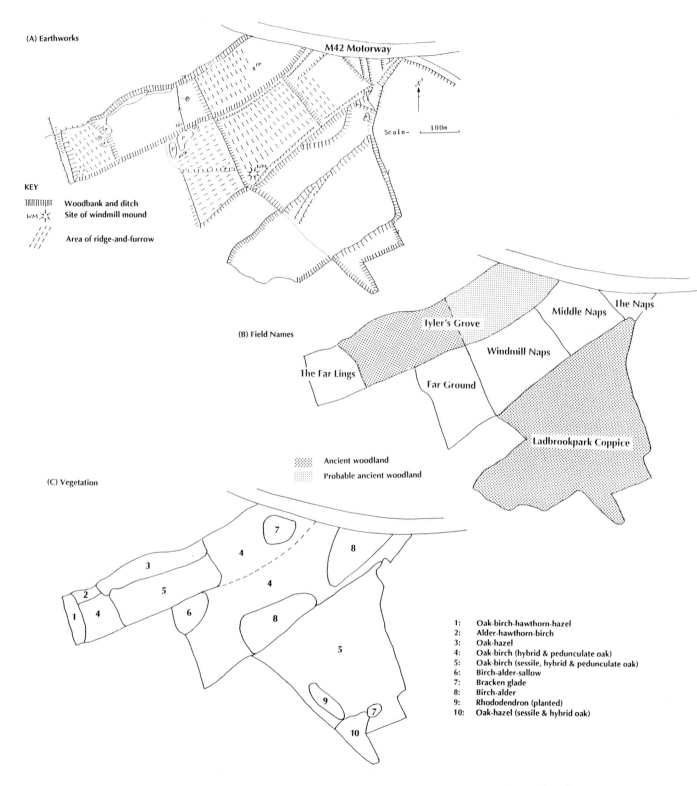

(A) Earthworks

M42 Motorway

Scale— |——| 100m

KEY

Woodbank and ditch
Site of windmill mound

Area of ridge-and-furrow

(B) Field Names

Tyler's Grove

Middle Naps

The Naps

The Far Lings

Windmill Naps

Far Ground

Ladbrookpark Coppice

Ancient woodland
Probable ancient woodland

(C) Vegetation

1: Oak-birch-hawthorn-hazel
2: Alder-hawthorn-birch
3: Oak-hazel
4: Oak-birch (hybrid & pedunculate oak)
5: Oak-birch (sessile, hybrid & pedunculate oak)
6: Birch-alder-sallow
7: Bracken glade
8: Birch-alder
9: Rhododendron (planted)
10: Oak-hazel (sessile & hybrid oak)

Evidence of Ancient Woodland at Windmill Naps: A: earthworks including woodbanks and ridge-and-furrow; B: field names from 18th century; C: vegetation pattern today. (DRM/AT, courtesy of Arlington Securities plc & Tarmac Properties Ltd)

Common cow-wheat, restricted to ancient woodlands in the north-west of the county. (JPW)

Wood and Hampton Wood. Where woods have expanded from their medieval boundaries, the original woodbank remains inside, with a new one typical of its period constructed at the new woodland edge. A whole sequence of differently aged woodbanks can therefore be seen in one wood, recording the changes in its size and shape. Such features can clearly be seen at Windmill Naps, where the wood expanded around 1800, and at Ryton Wood, where the central embanked third of the wood of about 70 acres may well be the same woodland noted for Ryton Parish in the Domesday Book.

In contrast some earthworks show that land has not always been wooded: it is therefore 'secondary' woodland, compared to the 'primary' woodland that has always remained wooded. The principal evidence for secondary woodland is the regular undulation of ridge-and-furrow agriculture. This method of farming indicates a long period of arable use of the land: where ridge-and-furrow exists within a wood then clearly that part of the wood must be secondary, probably naturally colonising during a period of agricultural decline. Such features can be seen in parts of Windmill Naps, Princethorpe, Hampton, and Chesterton Woods as well as many others. Similarly, archaeological remains of settlements within a wood indicate secondary woodland on that part at least, as at Tocil Wood near Warwick University. It is much more difficult to prove that woodland is primary wood, in that clearance of part of the wood at some stage in the past may not leave any trace on the ground. However, a study of earthworks and documentation shows that many Warwickshire woods have existed in the same place for at least seven hundred years.

To overcome the problem of deciding which woods are primary and which secondary, the term 'ancient woodland' has been coined. This generally refers to woodlands that have existed since before AD1600, although the year 1700 has also been suggested. It was only after these dates that plantations became popular, where people planted new woods in previously open areas. Before that woods were managed but not planted: if they expanded it was a natural expansion. Ancient woodlands are therefore also described as semi-natural – made up of wild plants but managed for wood and timber by people. They can be recognized, not only by woodbanks and earthworks, but also by the ancient coppice stools, often looking like a ring of young trees. Where the circle reaches four metres in diameter, as with small-leaved lime at Hartshill Hayes, Ryton or Oversley Wood, they represent individuals which may be 700 years old. Some plant species seem unable to colonise new woodlands, so their presence alone can indicate ancient woodland. Examples in the north and west of Warwickshire include small-leaved lime, wild service tree, sessile oak, common cow-wheat, and yellow archangel as well as the grasses wood melick and wood millet. In the south and east species such as woodruff, wood anemone and dog's mercury are more indicative. Current research shows that some animals too, like the rare woodland snails, may be confined to ancient woodland. These ancient woods have been described in heart-felt terms by Richard Mabey in *The Flowering of Britain*: 'These old woods, weather-beaten, hard-worked, spun about with legend and history, each one stocked with its own exclusive cargo of flowers, are life rafts out of the past'. They have been created by generations of continuous natural growth and human activity which has, uncommonly, benefited both.

In Warwickshire only few fragments now remain of the second important type of woodland management: wood pasture. This was a way of combining tree management with livestock production – a precarious business. It was the traditional land-use of wooded commons and deer parks as well as of Royal forests, probably the most misunderstood of all medieval management systems. Wood pastures today are rarely rich in flowering plants, but specialise in ancient trees which may be over 300 years old. These can be important as a habitat for rare

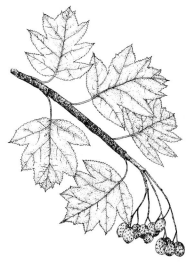

Wild service tree, a tree found in ancient woodlands and hedgerows.
(JPW)

lichens and insects, and also provide shelter for birds and bats. The trees are usually 'pollards', that is they have been regularly lopped at 2–3 metres from the ground to provide a wood crop safe from grazing livestock. Pollarding, like coppicing, seems to greatly extend the life of the tree.

Little is yet known of wooded commons in Warwickshire. The surviving Yarningale Common is wooded, but most of this is recent secondary woodland. Forty years ago much of the common was an excellent stretch of heath and gorse, but grazing was abandoned some years ago, and the trees have grown up. Part of the common does have oak-maple-hazel woodland with some larger oaks and woodland plants like bluebell and so may be older woodland, but it would be difficult to prove.

At some time before 1485 Warwickshire had at least 60 deer parks, mostly in the Arden area of the north-west. These were private land, often with an internal ditch and a 'pale' or fence of cleft oak to retain the (usually fallow) deer. The animals were kept for venison – a way of using poor, infertile land not suitable for arable or other pasture. Deer parks were also a powerful status symbol. Many parks had enclosed woods inside them, producing wood from coppice and pollards, and timber from larger trees. They often had areas for grazing cattle and sheep, areas for hay, and some even had quarries for stone.

Across all of England few of these ancient deer parks survive. Warwickshire's only remaining ones are post-medieval, such as the private Packington Park near Meriden, which still has a cleft oak paling, ancient oak trees, bracken glades and a thriving herd of fallow deer. There is also the National Trust's Charlecote Park, and Birmingham's Sutton Park. Here the surviving enclosed woods (or 'hursts') have long remained uncoppiced and so are the poorer for wildlife: some have even had conifers planted in them. Sometimes the only remains of a deer park are some ancient pollards, once part of the boundary, like the two oaks on the southern boundary of the former Knights Templar deer park at Temple Balsall. Similarly, at Pinley near Claverdon, old pollards survive in hedges on the site of the deer park there. At Stoneleigh the massive old pollard oaks survive from a 17th century deer park, but a 1597 estate map suggests that they were survivors of even older hedges, removed to leave the trees as an 'instant deer park'.

The Forest of Arden was, in popular imagination, a vast wood covering half of Warwickshire. In reality, medieval 'forests' often had no woodland at all, like the Forest of Dartmoor. The confusion has arisen because the meaning of the word has changed over time. These legal forests were simply areas where deer were protected under forest law. The 'forest' had nothing to do with trees at all. Even Sherwood Forest was mostly heathland with some small enclosed woods. Some forests, like Epping in Essex, had a core of woodland or wood pasture, but even here it was only a small proportion of the whole: Epping Forest had only 10% wood pasture, the remainder being farmland, villages and even including the town of Waltham Abbey. As forests were mainly legal entities (although not much good for protecting the deer), they could be created and destroyed – disaforested – by the stroke of a pen, with little or no impact on the ground.

The legal Forest of Arden is poorly documented, although referred to in 1148. It was probably short-lived and its exact legal boundaries are unknown, although place names like Henley-in-Arden and Hampton-in-Arden suggest the location. In 1086 the Arden area was only about one third wooded, and there is plenty of evidence from the next few centuries to show that wood clearance here was rapid and extensive. It is in fact quite possible that areas designated as legal forests lost their woodland at a greater rate than ordinary countryside. The Forest of Arden lives on in myths and folklore as a fairytale woodland; the reality was different.

A pollarded oak, typical of boundary markers of deer parks. (JPW)

Most of the ancient woods present in medieval Warwickshire persisted up to the 19th century. There were some periods of destruction, as in the period between 1800 and 1860 when Hampton Wood was reduced from 70 acres to its present 26 by clearance for farmland. Some other woods disappeared entirely. The strong tradition of pasturing animals in wood probably turned many of them into open commons and heaths, particularly in the Arden area. Many of these commons were then destroyed by enclosure or by the expansion of urban Birmingham. In 1895 Warwickshire had about 21,000 acres of woodland, including recent plantations, making about 3.5% of the county. In 1920 there were about 12,000 acres of intact ancient woodland but by 1985 only 6,000 acres remained as semi-natural woodland: some 1,300 acres had gone completely, and a further 4,500 acres had been converted into conifer plantations, effectively destroying most of the wildlife interest. The total loss of intact ancient woodland this century has therefore been nearly 50%.

Examples of complete losses include the 54 acres Fernhill Wood near Honiley, the 81 acres Frankton Wood near Stretton and High Wood, Brinklow, where 84 acres have been cleared from the centre of the wood, leaving a ring of trees around the edge. All these losses were for agriculture, but the 27 acre Hopyard Wood was destroyed for sand and gravel extraction, and the huge 94 acre Chelmsley Wood is now a housing estate. There are only five woods in the whole area over 250 acres, and four of them (Bentley Park, Hay, Weston and Waverley, and Oversley Woods) have all been extensively coniferised. Only Ryton remains unplanted. The many thousands of acres of new plantings during the last century cannot balance these irreplaceable ancient woods in terms of wildlife, history, or cultural importance. The remaining 'life rafts out of the past' are Warwickshire's finest wildlife features.

Ever since the first clearances of the wildwood for agriculture, the decline in woodland has been mirrored by an increase in land for farming, with two main uses: arable land for crops, and grassland for grazing livestock.

Arable farming has undergone many revolutionary changes, a key one for Britain being the development of 'open-field' or strip cultivation. This system of managing the land involved dividing up fields into strips or 'selions', each notionally half an acre: 220 yards long by 11 yards wide. Each farmer within a village would look after a selection of these strips, scattered around

THE FORMATION OF RIDGE-AND-FURROW FARMLAND

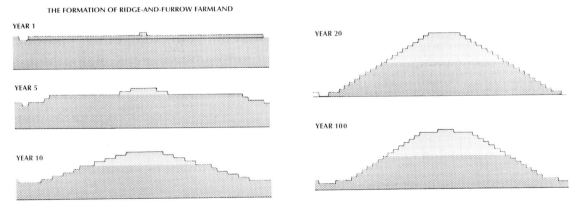

Ridge-and-furrow farmland was probably produced by the systematic ploughing of individual strips of land, as this computer simulation shows. Year 1: The first ploughing results in a small bank in the centre of each strip, with a ditch between strips. Years 5 & 10: The ridge becomes more pronounced and the furrow deeper. Year 20: The ridge-and-furrow pattern is formed. Year 100: The system is maintained as ploughing each year is balanced by erosion of the bare earth. (AT)

33

the fields of the village. The method of ploughing a selion altered the shape of the land, by creating a ridge along the length of each one, with a furrow along each side. Because of the difficulty in manoeuvering the ox ploughs of the time, a gently curving plough-line was created, in a reversed 'S' shape. There were few hedges separating fields, just headlands where the plough was turned, and access tracks of various kinds. Quite how this ridge-and-furrow system of farming came into being, or even when, is largely unknown. It is known in parts of England, Wales, France, and Germany; fossilised ridge-and-furrow of Viking times has also been found in Denmark. The Black Death, sweeping across Britain in the 1350s, caused much arable land to be abandoned to pasture, and the grass cover over this ridge-and-furrow has remained in many Warwickshire fields to this day, a vivid reminder of our past.

The importance of ridge-and-furrow for Warwickshire is that the county straddles a national boundary between the open-field or 'planned' countryside which extends in a wedge shape from Yorkshire to Somerset and then back to Norfolk, and the traditional small enclosed fields of 'ancient' countryside. The south-east Feldon region was the mainstay of open-field agriculture in the county, reaching up to the north of Rugby and Coventry. John Leland, writing in the first half of the sixteenth century, described this area as 'champion ground . . . somewhat barren of wood but very plentifull of corne . . . the Fieldon'. In contrast, traditional, small, irregular fields were characteristic of the Arden region in north-west Warwickshire: in Leland's words 'much enclosyed, plentifull of gres, but no great plenty of corne'. This difference between Feldon and Arden, well established by medieval times and clearly related to the underlying soils and geology, is still visible today.

The differences in farming caused differences in hedges: few in Feldon, many in Arden. Furthermore, the Arden hedgerows were often of ancient origin, or 'ghost' outlines of cleared woodland, both rich in tree and shrub species. Such hedgerows today may have five to 12 woody species in a 30 metre length, including species like midland hawthorn, small-leaved lime, and wild service. Holly hedges too are common. In the hedge bottom are woodland wild flowers such as bluebell, yellow archangel and primrose. Often the hedgerow trees have been coppiced or pollarded and follow a sinuous boundary on an old earthbank. Examples abound along the lanes of north-west Warwickshire, of what we could call 'life-lines out of the past'.

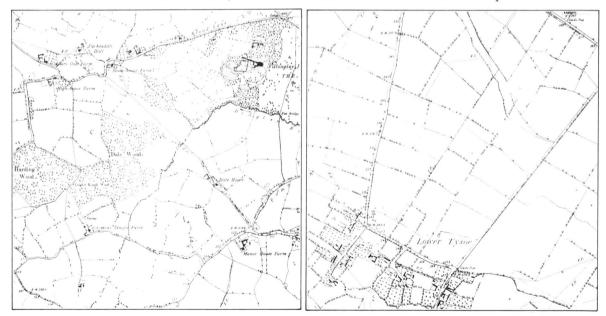

'Ancient' and 'planned' countryside A: the Arden area to the south-west of Fillongley Hall has all the characteristics of ancient countryside: sinuous patterns of woodland edges, hedgerows and roads. Dale Wood and Holbech's Wood are still the same today, but Harding's Wood and Leigh's Rough Wood are now farmland. B: The Feldon area north of Tysoe is typical of 'planned' countryside, mostly unwooded open fields that were enclosed in the 18th and 19th centuries with straight, planned, hedges and roads.
(1st edition Ordnance Survey, WRO.)

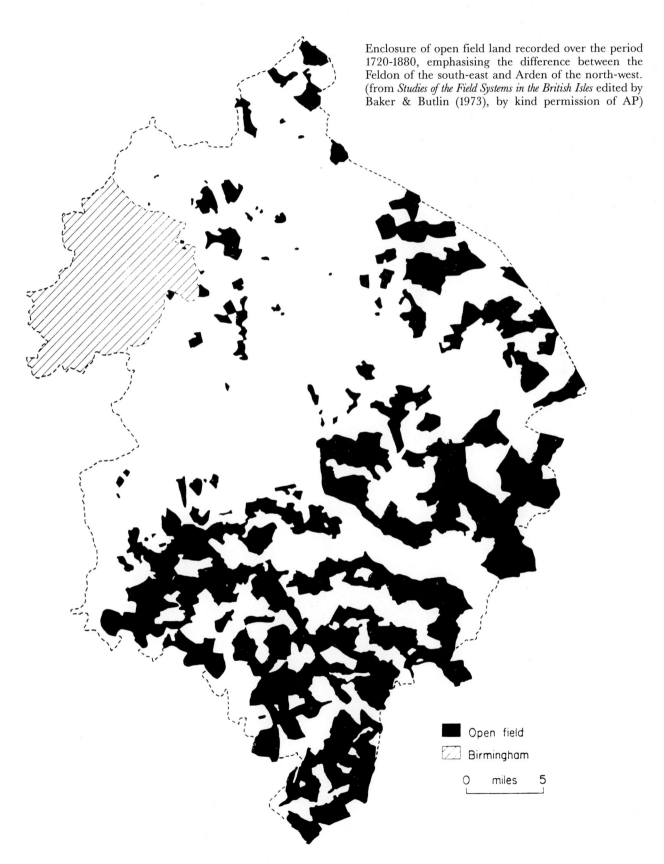

Enclosure of open field land recorded over the period 1720-1880, emphasising the difference between the Feldon of the south-east and Arden of the north-west. (from *Studies of the Field Systems in the British Isles* edited by Baker & Butlin (1973), by kind permission of AP)

Open field

Birmingham

0   miles   5

ABOVE LEFT: Small-leaved lime coppice stool at Hartshill Hayes Country Park. (CM) BELOW: 'Domesday Ditch' at Ryton Wood nature reserve. (MWF) ABOVE RIGHT: Ridge-and-furrow in the snow at Edge Hill. (MWF) BELOW: An old pollard oak in ridge-and-furrow pasture at Snitterfield. (MWF)

The Arden, largely open in medieval times, underwent a further revolution with the Enclosure Acts of Parliament between 1720 and 1880. These formalised a process which had been going on for some years, where previously open arable land was enclosed to keep in sheep and cattle, and often to keep out people. These new hedges were straight, planted mainly with hawthorn, and many are clearly evident, marching over ancient abandoned ridge-and-furrow. Such hedges are less good for wildlife than ancient hedgerows, as it can take many centuries for woody species to invade hedgerows. As an approximate rule of thumb, it is reckoned that a hedge gains one woody species in a 30 metre length every 100 years, so providing an approximate ecological hedge-dating system.

One of the county's most important hedgerows trees was the English elm, so widespread earlier this century as to give the name 'Leafy Warwickshire'. Dutch elm disease has now taken almost all the mature elms, but everywhere in hedges suckers are growing from the roots of the old trees, some reaching 8–10 metres tall. Even if these succumb to the disease as well, it is likely that further suckers will be produced until the epidemic has passed. Similar waves of elm disease have been and gone for many thousands of years and, although the current wave has been virulent, it is only the latest in a long line. The main threat now is the grubbing out of stumps and the grazing or cutting back of the regrowing shoots. Even wych elm, which does not sucker, is surviving in some places, ready to spread back to its former haunts. Left to their own devices, the elms of Warwickshire could again make the county leafy in another hundred years or so.

The historical development of grasslands in the county is difficult to trace before Domesday Book, where about 4,500 acres of meadow are recorded, mainly on the Feldon. Meadows – where the grass is cut for hay – became more valuable than arable by medieval times, and any piece of land near a stream or river was likely to have been managed in this way. Pasture – where the grass is grazed by livestock – would have been widespread on less-favoured land including commons, heaths, and wood pasture. From 1450 to 1550 much new pasture was created in the Feldon by landlords keen to cash in on the demand for wool. These meadows and pastures had a diversity of wild flowers as well as of grasses; John Speed, writing in 1600 at the same time as Shakespeare, described 'meadowing pastures with their green mantles so imbroidered with flowers that from Edg-Hill we may behold another Eden'.

By the late 18th century Warwickshire was known as a dairy county, the chief product being cheese, for which it was famous. The high price of corn in the Napoleonic wars caused much grass to be ploughed up, but by 1850 it was estimated that half of Warwickshire's farmland was permanent pasture. The proportion of grass increased so that, by 1904, 340,000 acres of permanent pasture compared to 150,000 acres of arable. Despite the 'plough up' policies of two world wars, flower-rich grassland was still common in the Warwickshire of 1950, part of a man-managed system of livestock production and wild flower conservation going back centuries.

In the Middle Ages there were many thousands of acres of heathland in Warwickshire, often common land owned by one person but with rights of grazing held by many. The land was usually poor, with sandy soils that could not readily be cultivated, and common grazing provided a sustainable return. It is not specifically recorded in the Domesday Book, although the entry for Wolvey includes 'pasture half a league in length and breadth' which could be the same Wolvey heath recorded in 1201–2 when Reynold Bassett gave to the Abbot of Coombe '100 acres of land in the heath of Wlveia . . . and in the heath of Wlveia pasture for 500 sheep'. This heath had a colourful history, with a hermitage founded on it in 1394; the hermit was to pray for the benefactors of Coombe Abbey. Later in 1555 Lady Smyth was publicly executed, by burning on the heath, for the murder of her husband. There was still heath at Wolvey in

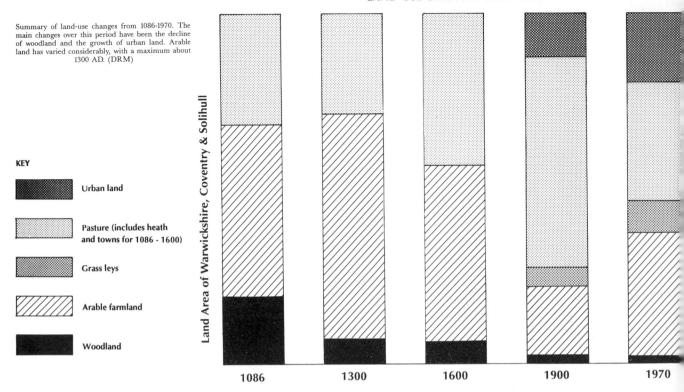

Summary of land-use changes from 1086-1970. The main changes over this period have been the decline of woodland and the growth of urban land. Arable land has varied considerably, with a maximum about 1300 AD. (DRM)

KEY

Urban land

Pasture (includes heath and towns for 1086 - 1600)

Grass leys

Arable farmland

Woodland

Land Area of Warwickshire, Coventry & Solihull

1086   1300   1600   1900   1970

1604, but it is likely it was destroyed not long after. In 1556 the manor of Rugby still had 1000 acres of 'rush ground and heath' and 20 of moor; as late as 1743 the lord of the manor there had the sole right of turves and gorse on a piece of Rugby Heath of 56 acres. Being largely open ground, heaths were often used as battlefields and parade grounds in the Civil War. For example, the new Royalist army mustered for the first time on Meriden Heath on 18 October 1642 just before the battle of Edge Hill. On 19 October, Prince Rupert signed his address as 'at Packington Heath'.

In the Arden area in 1603 the manor of Tamworth still had 100 acres of heath, divided between Aspley Heath, Ilshaw Heath, Hockley Heath, and Shirley Heath. Although Arden had more heaths than Feldon, the increasing enclosure of land from around 1600 converted many of them into low-grade farmland. Apart from Sutton Park, little remains today except place names to remind us of this characteristic habitat, with its unique range of plants and animals.

A final thread in the fabric of our past is the use made of Warwickshire's minerals. Stone for building and clay for tiles and bricks have been used since at least Roman times, but coal has had a much more dramatic impact on the north of the county. Although charcoal from coppice woods had been a key fuel for industry, by the early 1600s coal from Coventry was coming into its own, with many small mines at 'Hawkesberie' and Foleshill. Other mines stretched to the north through Bedworth and Griff to Chilvers Coton in Nuneaton. Across north Warwickshire to Polesworth and Kingsbury, coal mining over the next three hundred years had a major effect on shaping the land. The development of mines led to the building of turnpike roads, then canals, and then railways, all in turn impacting on the nature of this part of Warwickshire; a legacy for wildlife still present today. In the south and east, quarrying for limestone was also developed, leaving its mark too. More recently extensive sand and gravel quarries have had a marked effect on the nature of Warwickshire.

The signs of all these different habitats – woodland, grassland, heathland, and farmland – can thus be traced from the last Ice Age up to the present. The next chapters examine the plants and animals of these habitats, exploring how they live and where they are found.

ABOVE: Ancient woods also have many woodbanks and ditches, such as this in Ryton Wood nature reserve, here with small-leaved lime on it. (CM) LEFT: Small-leaved lime coppice can produce huge stools where coppicing has been continued for centuries, as this outgrown stool at Piles Coppice shows. (CM) RIGHT: Young coppice produces new shoots rapidly: this is one-year hazel at Hampton Wood nature reserve. (GA)

LEFT: Typical plants of ancient woods in Warwickshire include yellow archangel (JRR) RIGHT: and herb paris, with its pattern of symmetrical leaves. (JRR) BELOW: Old pollard oaks such as the Baginton Oak were often boundary markers. (CM)

ABOVE: Winter makes ridge-and-furrow fields that much easier to see: a 'fossilised' landscape first formed by farming and then unchanged since the Black Death of the 14th century. (MWF) BELOW: Dead elms characterised many hedges in the 1970s, like this one at Edge Hill. Now elms are growing well from suckers where grazing animals are excluded. (BSK)

ABOVE: Clowes Wood nature reserve was the first freehold property donated to the Trust. (JRR)
BELOW: Old Nun Wood nature reserve near Princethorpe was purchased by the Trust in 1984. (AT)

42

Woods and Coppice

And in the woods where you and I
Upon faint primrose beds were wont to lie

(CBH)

A Midsummer Night's Dream

The entirely natural deciduous forest of small-leaved lime, elm, oak, ash, alder and birch, which colonised Warwickshire after the last Ice Age, is now almost entirely gone. Even the more recent 'leafy Warwickshire' was hard-hit by Dutch elm disease. Sadly, just three per cent of the area is now wooded, one of the lowest proportions of any county in England. The real picture is even worse than this, because over half the woodland is conifer plantation of larch, pine and spruce. Close planting of these alien species leads to low light levels, deepening piles of fallen needles and acidification of the soil. The remaining broadleaved woods are therefore that much more important, valued by both people and wildlife alike.

Although trees are the obvious dominant plants, shrubs and wild flowers are also important components of the woodland system, providing food for a variety of animals. These herbivores range from tiny insects to larger mammals; some feed on a single species of plant and others eat almost anything. There are also many carnivorous predators from the tops of the trees down to the soil, again with a variety of feeding habits. Dead leaves and dead trees provide food for many other insects and small invertebrates, decomposing the plant material and so recycling its minerals. Fungi too play a key part here, their thread-like *hyphae* penetrating the decaying wood, producing reproductive toadstools in the autumn. At other times of the year birds invade, feeding on the wealth of small insects or berries. Varying from top to bottom, day to night, and summer to winter, woodlands are among the most complex of Warwickshire's habitats.

The north-western half of the county has more acidic, less fertile soils than the south-east, causing a marked difference in woodland types. In the old Arden area are woods with both sessile and pedunculate oak, small-leaved lime and both of the birches: silver birch on the drier sandy soils and downy birch in the damper places. Rowan, holly, and to a lesser extent buckthorn, make up the understorey. Good woods of this kind are found in Sutton Park, Kingsbury, Bentley Park, Hoar Park, Hartshill Hayes and Windmill Naps, with an outstanding example near to Earlswood – Clowes Wood. The Binley Woods area east of Coventry has Piles Coppice, Brandon, Birchley and New Close Woods, while Kenilworth has Crackley Wood.

Typical wild flowers of Warwickshire's woodlands: stichwort, red campion and bluebell. (JPW)

A prime block of woodland is located to the west of Princethorpe, where a clutch of magnificent woods still persists: Ryton, Wappenbury, Waverley, Bubbenhall, and Princethorpe Great Wood. Near, but not joining with each other, their linking would create a huge tract of woodland not seen in Warwickshire for over two thousand years.

All these woods share the beauty of bluebell, wood anemone, red campion, common dog violet and wood sorrel: a splash of spring colours. Later on there are frequent brambles, wood sage and honeysuckle, with three ferns – bracken, male fern and broad buckler fern – all widespread. Snowdrops are naturalised in many places, with Brandon Castle, Wolston a prime example. A few wild daffodils survive in Hay Wood but offer no competition to the conifers now there too. Lily-of-the-valley flourishes at Clowes Wood, along with common cow-wheat and bilberry: these two species are widespread elsewhere in Britain from Cornwall to the Scottish Highlands, but uncommon here in Warwickshire.

On the base-rich soils of the south, ash is often dominant, with pedunculate oak less frequent and sessile oak absent. Wych elm used to be common before the wave of Dutch elm disease took its toll, and in its wake took out the violet helleborine that once grew beneath the elms in Bannams Wood, Moreton Bagot. The shrub layer in these south-eastern woods comprises dogwood, hazel, wayfaring tree, midland hawthorn and even occasionally spindle, with its splendid orange and coral fruits.

Fine calcareous woods are found at Snitterfield, Hampton, Ufton, Chesterton, Withycombe, Oversley, Bannams, Whichford and Wolford. At Ufton – more correctly called Long Itchington & Ufton Wood – the continued coppicing and inherent wildlife value of the wood led to its inclusion in the national Nature Conservation Review, completed by the Nature Conservancy Council in 1976, one of only two sites in Warwickshire to be listed.

Typically, the lime-rich soils of these woods support a more diverse flora than those of the north-west. The poisonous dog's mercury, with its male and female flowers on separate plants, is typical of these woods, together with the more colourful lesser celandine, bugle and yellow archangel. In damper areas ramsons may be detected by its garlic smell before it is seen, carpeting the ground with starry white flowers. Primroses form carpets too, drifts of pale yellow through Hampton Wood. Where cowslips occur nearby, the hybrid false oxlip may be found, with its characteristics halfway between both parents. Primroses also attract the attention of the common bee-fly, whose furry tawny body and black-edged wings can be seen hovering in front of the flowers as it sucks the nectar. Less tranquil is the feeding habit of its larva, which is a parasite on solitary bees, sucking them dry.

Lime in the soil encourages many orchids, with early purple orchids complementing the bluebells in many places, although lesser butterfly orchid only occurs in Ufton Wood, and the saprophytic bird's nest orchid is only found here and at Oakley Wood. This bird's nest orchid – named because of the tangled mat of its roots – has no chlorophyll at all, so no green colour; it exists entirely by absorbing decaying materials through its roots. Purple flowers of broad-leaved helleborine appear here and there in a number of woods, but its white-flowered relative, the narrow-leaved helleborine, is only found in Oversley Wood near Alcester. The rarest of all must be the fly orchid, whose sighting at Snitterfield Bushes in 1988 was the first Warwickshire record for over a hundred years.

Other wild flower rarities include herb paris, with its characteristic leaf pattern, found in a few woods and well guarded Kineton military camp. Stinking hellebore is found at Alveston

Primroses carpet the ground at Hampton Wood nature reserve. (HC)

44

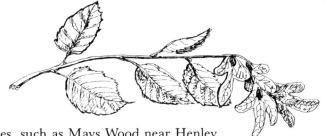

Hornbeam is not common in the county. (PJC)

Pastures near Loxley, while green hellebore has more sites, such as Mays Wood near Henley in Arden and Bannams Wood too. The aptly named stinking iris graces the woods around Billesley, looking good, first with its flowers and then its berries. Autumn brings the meadow saffron in flower at Snitterfield Bushes and at Weethley Wood on the county boundary west of Dunnington.

The uncommon wild service tree still grows in a number of woods – Spernal Park, Hartshill Hayes, Oversley and Hanging Wood near Claverdon – as well as in ancient hedgerows. Hornbeam is an infrequent tree too, usually found alone except at All Oaks Wood, Brinklow, where it paradoxically occurs in profusion as an abandoned hornbeam coppice. Beech is nowhere native in the county, although the hangers at Edge Hill feel almost like the Cotswold beech woods. A fine stand occurs at Clowes Wood, where the co-existing fungi are spectacular in the autumn.

Sycamore is common throughout the county: a handsome tree when mature, its prolific offspring can dramatically alter the nature of a wood, changing an oak woodland into a sycamore woodland in less than fifty years. Introduced to Britain in the Middle Ages, sycamore still supports little variety of wildlife and conservation management to remove it is important where it threatens to take over.

In the past, Warwickshire's woods were intensively managed as coppice with oak standards, encouraging a flush of spring flowers after coppicing was completed. Coppice management became uneconomic only in the last fifty years, yet the practice has now all but gone. Ufton Wood has uniquely continued to be coppiced and has now been joined by many Trust reserves, where the traditional cutting rotation has been reintroduced, often with spectacular results for wild flowers.

Mosses are common in most woods, the damp, shady conditions well-suited to their reproduction. Some, like hair moss, thrive in the acid north-west, whereas others, such as *Rhytidiadelphus triquetrus*, need the more lime-rich soils of the south-east. It is unfortunate that more mosses do not have common English names, as their delicate forms might then be more appreciated.

Common fungi of woodland include the fly agaric – the fungus always drawn with pixies on them – and the birch bracket fungus, both widespread in birch woods, sulphur tufts on dead stumps and stinkhorns, with unpleasant fly-attracting odour. Less common are the earth stars at Waverley Wood and the Trust's Temple Balsall nature reserve.

Many insects and other invertebrates of woodland are dependent on the presence of single species of plants for their survival, but more complex stories emerge, as the plants themselves are affected by the way the woodland is managed. Coppice, for example, brings in light on a regular basis, so encouraging many wild flowers and their associated insects. As the coppice wood grows, so shading increases and both the flowers and insects decline. The way that the woodland's rides and glades are managed affects insects too, as does the presence of ageing trees and dead wood. In general, because of the continuity of woodland cover, ancient woods provide the best habitats for a wide range of woodland invertebrates, particularly beetles and true flies.

Changes in management, or general neglect of management, have been the main cause of the decline and disappearance of all the breeding colonies of fritillary butterflies from our county within the last thirty years. Other factors, such as changes in microclimate and humidity, may also have played a part in the demise of these beautiful orange and brown butterflies, but they are difficult to prove. High brown fritillaries were last resident in

Ground beetles feed on the many woodland invertebrates. (WNCT)

Warwickshire in 1958, small pearl-bordered fritillaries in 1960, and pearl-bordered in 1968. The silver-washed fritillary hung on until the early 1970s. Although odd ones have been seen since, and some re-introduction attempted, it does not now breed in Warwickshire. All these fritillaries lay their eggs on dog violet, a common enough woodland plant, but the butterflies need precisely the right degree of shading for breeding to be successful. Abandoned coppice, or lack of clearance of woodland rides, means the violet becomes too shaded, and the butterfly ceases to breed.

The white admiral butterfly, in contrast, has shown a series of expansions here. Arriving in Warwickshire in the early part of this century it underwent a large extension of its range in the early 1950s, followed by a contraction in the sixties. The early eighties saw it extend its range once more, spreading into woods never before occupied. This might also be related to changes in woodland management, as the white admiral depends solely on honeysuckle growing in shady places as its larval food plant, and the abandonment of coppice has led to an increase in shaded honeysuckle. The butterfly's strongholds in Warwickshire are Ryton Wood (its first recorded colony), Wappenbury Wood, and Wolford Wood straddling the Gloucestershire border. The young caterpillars feed mainly at night, spending the daylight hours quite still along the underside of the leaf, resembling nothing more than a shrivelled fragment of the leaf itself. After a few month's growth they hibernate in a shelter made from honeysuckle leaves bound to the plant stem with silk, then in spring they emerge and feed until they pupate in June, the adults feeding on bramble in July and August.

Of the five British hairstreak butterflies, four have been found in the county. The brown hairstreak had only a short history, being recorded first in 1970 and last in 1972. A butterfly often active at the top of woodland canopies, flying only in bright sunshine, it lays its over-wintering eggs solely on exposed blackthorn. At its last Warwickshire site the blackthorn was shaded out by other trees, and an adjacent suitable hedgerow suffered from drastic annual winter trimming. In contrast the purple hairstreak, which is an oak-feeder, is found in many oak woods and has been re-discovered in the north and west of the county in the 1980s. The white-letter hairstreak caterpillars feed strictly on elms and remain uncommon, whereas the green hairstreak, with broader tastes, is more widespread.

The management of woodland rides is a crucial factor for butterflies. Open sunny rides, glades and clearings may be populated in summer with fifteen or more species: meadow brown, ringlet, gatekeeper, speckled wood, wall brown, small heath, small copper and even the occasional marbled white. Grassy areas also attract common blues, large and small skippers, and orange tips, with brimstones widespread in most woods where its foodplants − buckthorn or alder buckthorn − are present. The wood white, another woodland-edge species, remains uncommon in this county.

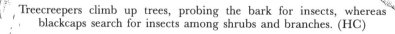

Treecreepers climb up trees, probing the bark for insects, whereas blackcaps search for insects among shrubs and branches. (HC)

The larger woods of Warwickshire support good populations of moths, although some small woods can be important too: the 26-acre Hampton Wood has produced 325 species out of the county total of 560. These include such nationally scarce species as the alder kitten, brown scallop, dotted rustic, lead-coloured drab and silver cloud. Hampton is also one of only two sites in the county for the orange moth, seen in 1986 after a break of 47 years.

Oversley Wood has been one of the richest sites in the Midlands for moths, with six nationally notable species present, most dependent on aspen. Aspen has a number of insects which feed solely on it, the rarest being a beetle (*Zeugophora flavicollis*) recorded in Warwickshire in 1988 after a gap of ten years from anywhere in Britain. Snitterfield Bushes had a new county record in 1989 when the beautiful snout moth was found there. Other woodland moths of interest include the great oak beauty, great prominent, pale November moth, barred hooktip, popular and satin lutestrings and angle-striped sallow: wonderful names for beautiful insects.

Most Warwickshire woods also support a wide range of other common woodland insects, such as the oak bush-cricket, with huge but harmless ovipositor, bracken bug and hawthorn shield-bug, with feeding preferences for single plants and wood boring beetles whose larvae chew their way through dead and decaying timber. Swarms of longhorn moths fly around bushes under oaks and carnivorous ground beetles eat everything within reach of their powerful jaws.

Ryton Wood is also home to a number of rare insects, including two hoverflies that are considered to be vulnerable to extinction on a national scale. These species, the small blue-black *Psilota anthracina* and the bronzy *Ferdinandea ruficornis*, are now so localised in their European distribution that their presence indicates woods of considerable importance; Ryton scores again.

Not all Warwickshire's woodland insects are associated with broadleaved woodlands; several conifer-dependent species occur here too. Probably the most spectacular is the giant woodwasp, a harmless 25mm long mimic of the hornet, with a bright orange and black body. The females, sometimes known as 'horntails', have a long and dangerous-looking ovipositor at the rear of their body. Thankfully this is not designed for stinging, but for boring through bark in order to lay eggs in the soft sap-wood. The males are duller in colour and seldom seen, staying high in the tree-tops at places like Brandon Wood and Coombe Abbey. A much more unexpected find at Brandon Wood was a small black sawfly (*Microdiprion pallipes*) sighted in 1987. Until then this sawfly had only ever been recorded in Britain from the Scottish pine forests of Inverness, and this Brandon specimen was a first for England. A few plants depend on conifers too, such as the yellow bird's nest at Moreton Morrell, Ufton Fields and Wilmcote Rough.

For many birds, the structure of a woodland is of much greater importance than the tree species present. Those with open canopies and well-developed shrub and ground layers support the most birds, while denser woods with no shrub layer – such as conifer plantations – support the fewest. Conifers are good for species such as coal tits and goldcrests, but deciduous woods will commonly have wood pigeon, wren, robin, blackbird, blue tit and great tit, carrion crow, magpie, chaffinch and greenfinch.

The best time to look for woodland birds is in the spring, when their singing makes location and identification that much easier among the bare branches, as they stake out their territories, inspect nest sites, and begin building. This is the time to listen for the drumming of woodpeckers. The most common of the three species in Warwickshire is the greater spotted woodpecker, which frequently excavates its nest hole in birch trees, often just below a bracket fungus. The lesser spotted woodpecker is the scarcest, smallest and most easily overlooked as it tends to feed high in the woodland canopy. Often it excavates its nest in a branch rather than the main trunk, at woodlands such as Clowes Wood, Ryton Wood or Hampton Wood. The green woodpecker is the largest and least arboreal of the three but nevertheless its ringing laugh or 'yaffle' is to be heard in many open woods, particularly in the south-east of the county. Its nest is high up in a tree trunk, but it spends much of its time on the ground, searching for its favourite food – ants.

Tawny owl, found in many Warwickshire woods, feed mainly on small mammals and worms. (CBH)

Nuthatches are not common in Warwickshire but their strident calls can be heard ringing around those woods that have plenty of mature trees as at Leek Wootton. Climbing head-first up and down the bark looking for insects, they nest in holes in the tree, plastering mud around the entrance to keep the hole small. Treecreepers, on the other hand, are quieter but more widespread, occurring among trees of almost any age. Their nest may be behind bark or ivy, and they use their tail as a support when they climb up the bark probing for food. Marsh tits much prefer mature woodland where they search for seeds among a rich shrub layer, but willow tits are more often found among birch or other scrub in damp situations. At dusk woodcocks indulge in their unique 'roding' flights just above the tree-tops, in either broadleaved or coniferous woods. Where the woodland canopy is patchy, starlings and stock doves are found.

Summer visitors begin to arrive back at the woods just as the first leaves are opening. Chiffchaffs and willow warblers are the first to get back, sometimes as early as March but usually in April. Both species are widespread throughout the county, though the chiffchaff is more at home among the upper canopy of mature trees and the willow warbler among the lower scrub. May is the peak month for bird song. By this time blackcaps and garden warblers have arrived to add their voice to the dawn chorus. Garden warblers much prefer an open situation whereas blackcaps will tolerate a closed canopy as long as there is still plenty of shrub cover. Cuckoos too will be in full voice as they move stealthily about, keeping a watchful eye on prospective hosts. The last of the summer visitors to arrive is the spotted flycatcher, a delicate and unobtrusive little bird, often seen near woodland ponds or streams, searching out insects.

Two typical woodland predators of our area are sparrowhawk and tawny owl, both widespread across the county. Sparrowhawks were common in the early 1950s, despite constant persecution, but began to decline nationally in the late fifties and early sixties, disappearing from more than a dozen counties in the east and south. This decline was the effect of persistent organo-chlorine pesticides which became concentrated up the food chain, poisoning these magnificent birds of prey. Fortunately the banning of these chemicals and the legal protection of the bird in 1963 led to a recovery and it is now getting back to its former levels. Tawny owls, feeding on a more mixed diet of small mammals, worms, and occasional birds, were not as affected. Other predators found in woodlands include kestrel, little owl and less commonly hobby and barn owl.

Of the less common woodland birds, hawfinch remain elusive but small numbers are seen from time to time in well-wooded parkland at places like Compton Verney. They favour seeds of hornbeam, holly and yew and it could be that somewhere there is a small breeding population. Nightingales still maintain their tenuous hold in the south of the county at places such as Ufton and Weethley Woods, and around the Shipston-on-Stour area, although their numbers have fallen in recent years. This may well be due to the decline in coppice management, but whether it will remain in numbers when newly coppiced areas in Trust nature reserves reach this age remains to be seen.

The other woodland specialists are that characteristic trio of upland oak woods – redstart, wood warbler and pied flycatcher. All are scarce in Warwickshire. The redstart was once more widely, if thinly, distributed but has declined and contracted, and now is down to one or two pairs in the acid oak woods of the north-west and Sutton Park. Wood warblers can sometimes be quite widespread in spring, and their sibilant song may give the impression that they are breeding. However, most singing birds are merely on passage and the number actually breeding remains small, with Clowes and Grendon Woods likely spots. So far the pied flycatcher has not bred in Warwickshire this century but the species is spreading and resplendent males have been seen in full song in Clowes and Bentley Park Woods, so one day it may yet breed in one of these more acid woodlands.

As the summer progresses so the woodland birds become less obvious. Song diminishes once there are young to be fed, fledglings are quickly removed to the relative safety of the upper canopy and many adults go into moult. By autumn, activity increases again as the resident birds start to form their winter feeding flocks. Soon they are joined by winter visitors which come in search of food and shelter. It is at this stage that the type of wood becomes important, as several species have marked feeding preferences.

Jays are most noticeable in autumn as they move about burying acorns for later retrieval, and long-tailed tits, which depend less on trees than other tits in the summer, often come into the woods at this time to forage through the upper shrub layer. Indeed mixed flocks of tits and finches, flitting restlessly through the canopy, or acrobatically feeding from the slenderest of twigs, are a feature of Warwickshire woodlands in winter. Birch seed is an especially favoured food of tits but other species, such as goldcrest and occasionally tree creeper and lesser spotted woodpecker, may join their feeding flocks. Some finches, such as goldfinch, redpoll and siskin, also feed on birch

Jays are widespread in woodlands, and some even venture into gardens.
(WNCT)

A nut-shell on the ground can show which animal has eaten it. (HC)

HAZELNUTS

Squirrel   Wood mouse

Woodpecker   Great Tit   Nuthatch

BEECHMAST

Wood mouse   Nuthatch

ROSE HIPS

Squirrel   Wood mouse

seed, but siskin much prefer alder at places like Ufton Fields and Stockton Cutting and the Tame Valley where they can be found throughout the winter in the company of redpoll.

Beech woods may seem devoid of birds in the summer but they come into their own in winter, when beech seed, or 'mast', becomes an important food source. The isolated areas of beech in the county may attract large feeding flocks, with great tits feeding on the fallen seed, joined by chaffinches and even the occasional brambling.

Berries are an equally important source of winter food, and blackbirds, song thrushes, redwings and fieldfares all come in search of hips, haws, holly and elderberries, especially in a hard winter. Woodcock are more numerous and widespread in winter too, and might occasionally be flushed from their camouflage of dead bracken during the day or be seen leaving to feed at dusk in Wappenbury, Withycombe and Whichford Woods. In the north, Atherstone Golf Course sounds an unlikely place to see woodcock, but they regularly come 'roding' out of the Merevale Woods and onto the fairways. Even where the winter woods lack a good food source, they may still be used as a roost for flocks of pigeons, thrushes, crows, starlings and finches, flying in at dusk and swirling around the darkening sky before settling down for the night.

Also roosting in the woods are bats, feeding at night on the many nocturnal insects over woodland and fields. Most widespread are the tiny pipistrelle and larger noctule, although occasional barbastelle or serotine may also be seen. They roost by day in holes in trees and cracks behind bark, in woods from Hoar Park to Ettington Park, although Coombe Abbey has probably the best range of species due to the proximity of wood, grassland, water and suitable buildings.

Most ancient woods support good populations of three small mammals – the wood mouse, yellow-necked mouse and bank vole, recently surveyed in Hanging Wood. Despite their generally similar appearance these animals have slightly different feeding habits, so reducing the competition between them. Mice can climb quite high in the canopy, searching for seeds and insects, while voles tend to stay nearer the ground, preferring leaves, bark and fruit. Foxes feed on these small mammals as well as birds, eggs, rabbits, insects and carrion, lying by day under scrub and hunting at dusk from woods throughout the county. The most endearing mammal, the badger, is also still widespread in the county, despite various threats. At least half its diet is made up of worms, supplemented with a range of plant materials from bluebell bulbs and hazel nuts to berries and grain. Living in underground setts that may have taken hundreds of years to build and extend, they have a regular system of paths leading to favoured feeding sites within their territory. Many young badgers are killed on roads as they search for new territories and, despite their legal protection, badgers also face persecution from some people in the name of sport. Increasingly vigilant protection will be needed to maintain Warwickshire's largest surviving native mammal.

Woodmouse with honeysuckle. (CBH)

Fallow deer in deer parks such as Packington and Charlecote are very much managed herds, but a few fallow occur in the wild too. The only common deer is the tiny muntjac, about the size of a large dog. Imported from China to Woburn in Bedfordshire in 1900, it escaped and began to breed in the wild. It has now spread throughout Warwickshire wherever there is good cover, and its preference for young shoots is having a marked impact on new coppice growth.

The new resurgence of coppice management in Trust-owned woods makes the future of at least some of our ancient woodlands that much more secure. However, with so many people, and so few good woods, compared to Shakespeare's days, lying on 'faint primrose beds' is certainly not to be encouraged!

Badgers – Warwickshire's most endearing mammal? (CBH)

51

LEFT: Fly orchids occur at only one site in Warwickshire: the Trust-owned Snitterfield Bushes nature reserve. (JRR) BELOW: Hartshill Hayes, now a Country Park managed by Warwickshire County Council, is an excellent sessile oak and small-leaved lime woodland, although some conifers have been planted. (AT) CENTRE: Narrow-leaved helleborine is also found only at one site in the county, a Forestry Commission woodland. (JRR) RIGHT: Sulphur tuft fungus grows on dead stumps of most trees, rotting the wood and recycling the minerals. (TH)

RIGHT: Primroses carpet the ground in Hampton Wood nature reserve.
(JRR) LEFT: Jays breed in most oak woodlands. (ML) CENTRE:
Bluebell glade at Ryton Wood nature reserve. (KR) BELOW: Fly agaric
is widespread in birch woods. (JRR)

53

Bracken thrives throughout the county, especially on sandy soils as at
Meriden Shafts. (BSK)

LEFT: White admiral butterflies have recently expanded in Warwickshire but are still not common. (CM) CENTRE: Speckled wood butterflies are common in all woods and shady corners. (CM) RIGHT: The common spotted longhorn beetle feeds on nectar, its larvae feeding in the dead wood of birch trees. (CM) BELOW: Woodland management used to be intensive: these eight people photographed in about 1900 worked full-time on the Dunchurch estate. (JSR)

LEFT: Greater spotted woodpeckers feed on insects under bark, making a characteristic drumming sound in most large woods. (FCM) ABOVE: Bank voles are typical of woodland. (FCM) RIGHT: Tawny owl feeding on a wood mouse. (FCM) BELOW: Badgers emerging from their sett. (FCM)

Among the Meadows

(CBH)

When daisies pied and violets blue,
And lady smocks, all silver-white,
And cuckoo-buds of yellow hue,
Do paint the meadows with delight

Love's Labour's Lost

Before the Second World War, Warwickshire had hundreds of pastures and meadows, which had existed almost unchanged for generations, if not centuries. They were rich in wild flowers, grasses, butterflies and other insects. To the passing eye Warwickshire today still has lots of green fields but these are the rich, lush green of heavily fertilised grass, sprayed with herbicides to kill off unwanted broad-leaved species. More cattle and sheep can now be stocked per acre, more silage can be made, but the cattle no longer walk through wild flowers up to their flanks and the haywains no longer creak with blossom.

In the wildwood, grassy clearings would have occurred long before people began their systematic deforestation in prehistoric times. These natural grasslands would have been grazed by the large herbivores then present in Britain. The now extinct auroch – a predecessor of domesticated cattle – and European bison or 'wisent' would have wandered among these glades, along with more familiar roe and red deer. Hares and small rodents such as bank vole, harvest mouse and yellow-necked mouse would also have spent their lives feeding on seeds, leaves, stems and fruit of the plants in these openings. It is the impact of all these grazing animals that allows and encourages grassland to exist.

Large grazing animals feed almost continually on the leaves and shoots of plants. For species such as trees and shrubs this usually spells death, as their woody stems cannot keep regenerating new leaves. For the grasses, as for a host of other wild flowers with growing shoots close to the ground, grazing simply checks their growth for a week or two. New leaves are then formed from the protected buds, and the plant continues to thrive. In this way are the plants of grassland different from the plants of the woods. If for any reason grazing stops, then the natural process of succession starts again, with shrubs and other woody species invading to produce first scrub and then woodland.

In Warwickshire as elsewhere, people cleared larger areas for grassland to support their domesticated livestock, and the plants from the natural clearings colonised these new grasslands. With time, sophisticated methods of managing the grass were also developed: hay meadows, where the grass was cut in mid-summer and dried to provide a winter feed for the livestock; flood meadows, where natural flood water was encouraged to stay and spread its fertile silt over the land, and water meadows, where a complex series of channels were dug to

Cowslip. (CBH)

divert water through riverside grasslands to give a better early growth and higher yield. Where grasslands were grazed instead of being cut for hay, the term 'pasture' was used: plants here were often prevented from flowering by the constant grazing, but a wide range of species flourished nevertheless, spreading vegetatively with runners, rhizomes, bulbs and corms. These traditional techniques have all but gone from Warwickshire, in the quest for greater grass yields using artificial fertilisers, and with them have gone most of the wild flower species that depended on them.

It was the hay meadows that used to give Warwickshire its great treasure of wild flowers. Over 97% of those present in the whole of Britain in the 1940s have now gone, with local losses at Sambourne, Claverdon, Long Itchington and Brailes. With them went grasses such as crested dogstail, sweet vernal grass, timothy, meadow foxtail and yellow oat-grass. Among the grasses was a wealth of colourful flowers: the yellows of cowslip, dandelion and cat's-ear, purples of spear thistle and knapweed, whites and pinks of white clover, lady's smock and common spotted orchid. Shakespeare's description is as true today as it was in 1600, even if we now call 'cuckoo-buds' buttercups instead. Occasionally fields with these wild flowers still persist in Warwickshire but their survival increasingly requires active protection as well as a continuation of the traditional management practice of hay making. This simple process of cutting the grass in June or July, letting it dry in the field, and then gathering it up into haystacks for winter feeding, had been practised for centuries. After the hay was cut it was customary to graze the late-season growth, or 'aftermath', taking the stock off the field only when there was no more grazing to be had, and putting them back for an early spring feed before 'shutting up' the meadows for hay in April.

The remaining jewel of Warwickshire's hay meadows is at Draycote near Dunchurch, where every May thousands of green-veined orchids join the mass of other wild flowers flourishing on this Trust-owned nature reserve. The yellow hay rattle is everywhere too, named from the sound of its seeds rattling around the dried seedheads at hay-making time. It is officially described as a hemi-parasite; although it has green leaves and so should be able to grow like any other plant, it links its roots to other species, possibly to tap their water or nutrients. Also flourishing still at Draycote are bird's-foot-trefoil, lady's mantle, yarrow, autumnal hawkbit and two rare ferns, adder's tongue and moonwort. Both these tiny plants are different from other ferns, with a single leaf about six centimetres high and a single central reproductive stalk.

Adder's tongue has an oval leaf with cylindrical lobed stalk, and moonwort a divided leaf and branching stalk. Although it was never common in the county, moonwort is now facing extinction, with Draycote its last known remaining site. The importance of these meadows is shown by their inclusion in the national Nature Conservation Review along with Ufton Wood.

Other hay meadows at Shadowbrook near Bickenhill are slightly damper, with great burnet mixed with meadow thistle, betony and pepper saxifrage. Each of these is now uncommon in the county – their combined presence points to the value of these meadows, now also owned by the Trust. A third important meadow in the south of the county at Oxhouse Farm near Combrook has a more lime-rich soil and a sympathetic owner. There quaking grass, woolly thistle, wild carrot, musk mallow, and common restharrow add to the more usual hay meadow species. In contrast, the few hay meadows on more acid soils, towards the west of the county at Dean's Green nature reserve, Ullenhall and Shelley Green, support heath spotted orchid as well as great burnet and devil's-bit scabious. Shelley Green is not just a hay meadow, however; it is a symbol of the many problems facing unimproved grasslands in our rapidly developing part of the world.

Green-veined orchid thrive at Draycote Meadows nature reserve. (WNCT)

Due to a catalogue of mistakes, the importance of Shelley Green was not emphasised to the right people at the right time. Consequently, planning permission was given for a hypermarket to be built on part of it, despite a public inquiry. Faced with a choice of watching it disappear under concrete and tarmac or trying to do something, the Trust opted for the latter approach, and two acres of meadow were moved six miles up the M42 to a new site. This mammoth task was completed in a six week period of rain and snow from the end of February to April 1987, with financial assistance from the hypermarket developers and the Nature Conservancy Council, together with a massive effort by Trust volunteers and Manpower Services Commission workers. Two acres of meadow still remain, behind the hypermarket and garden centre, surrounded by a three metre-high fence and now protected as a Site of Special Scientific Interest. The transported meadow has fared less well; some of the orchids are still surviving but the meadow's appearance has changed as the plants have altered their dominance. Moving meadows is clearly not a substitute for leaving them where they have been for centuries.

Permanent pasture, although not so visually attractive because flowers are often grazed off, can still make an excellent habitat for wild flowers, as one of the two fields at Draycote Meadows and the hills at Burton Dassett can testify. In practice it seems likely some old pastures were occasionally cut, and some meadows grazed instead of cut, so there are many species in common to both types of management, simply differing in relative abundance. For example, annuals such as hay rattle tend to grow better in meadows because they can set more seed, and there are more gaps on the ground for germination when the hay has been harvested; adder's tongue fern seems to do rather better in unimproved permanent pasture, as it can spread with an extensive underground rhizome system, but is not tall enough to compete with hay meadow plants.

With the demise of these traditionally-managed grassy habitats, so the remaining unimproved grassland takes on an extra importance. In Warwickshire the greatest area of this unimproved grass is found along the county's roads and railways, with additional newly-created habitats in quarries and spoil heaps.

Lacing the road verges early in the year will be cow parsley, later with huge stems of hogweed and gently arching flower-heads of false oat-grass, and on the lime-rich soils, the yellow of wild parsnip. Other grasses common on our verges include cocksfoot, meadow foxtail, smooth and rough meadow-grass, and creeping fescue. Depending on the soil type, verges also support knapweed, yarrow, common sorrel, bird's-foot trefoil, common vetch and ribwort plantain. Some stretches of the more southerly Fosse Way are aglow with meadow cranesbill, whereas in the north-east the foxglove provides welcome colour throughout midsummer. Road verge rarities include wild liquorice near Bishops Tachbrook, common rockrose near Lighthorne, and pyramidal orchid near Pillerton Priors. Less welcome invaders from another continent are Japanese knotweed and Himalayan balsam, the latter spreading persistently on some verges near Corley. Although verges provide some of the last semi-natural grassland in the county, with rare or uncommon plants and insects, too often they are treated simply as waste ground to be tipped on, dug up, or to be blandly suburbanised with planted daffodils or conifers.

A road verge at Binton, near to Welford-on-Avon shows it is possible to manage verges differently. In 1946 a shortage of funds meant a road-widening scheme on the A439 opposite Binton Station was left unfinished. There was no money for topsoil and the usual rye-grass-based seed mix was not sown. Instead the verge soil – a lias clay – was left to colonise naturally. Little is known of the first twenty years, but by the mid-sixties the nautre of the verge was evident. Encouraged by the south-facing aspect, butterflies abounded, including meadow brown and hedge brown as well as less common marbled white and all four Warwickshire species of skipper: large, small, grizzled and dingy. Common blue was also present, and even a clouded yellow butterfly was seen in 1979. A total of eight different species of woodlouse have been listed,

Once common on many roadside verges: meadow brown butterfly, tormentil and common spotted orchid. (HC)

including the first county record of one such (*Armadillidium nasatum*). The verge also boasts five species of orchid: twayblade, greater butterly, common spotted, bee, and at one time pyramidal orchids. Among broad-leaved species, the flowers of spiny rest-harrow, slender bird's-foot trefoil, carline thistle and blue fleabane have added their own colours and excitement. Disaster struck in 1978 when topsoil was spread over part of the verge, to complete the job begun 32 years before. However, the error was pointed out and the topsoil removed with no lasting damage, and the verge is now regularly managed by Trust volunteers to ensure this valuable habitat is maintained.

The natural colonisation of Binton verge, with no applied topsoil at all, points the way forward for other verges – or open spaces – throughout the county. These could either be left to colonise naturally, or the process speeded up by sowing wild flower seeds of the appropriate species. In fact, both these approaches have already been started, with no soil or seeds applied to a new verge at Red Hill on the A422 west of Stratford-on-Avon, and wild flower seed sown at Wyken Croft and Whitefriars Museum, Coventry and various open spaces in Nuneaton.

Probably the most spectacular grassy areas in the county are those naturally developed on old industrial workings, especially old limestone quarries, and old railway cuttings through the lime-rich lias clays. Many of these sites are now nature reserves and some also Sites of Special Scientific Interest because of their special wild flowers and insects. These reserves illustrate well the natural process of succession, where grassland is slowly invaded by scrub and then woodland, if there is no management work carried out. Grazing by sheep, as at Ufton Fields nature reserve, maintains the open grassland, but where there is no grazing, as at Harbury Spoilbank, hawthorn scrub quickly invades to shade out the grassland species. Conservation management has to weigh up the value of grass and scrub, and then try to achieve the optimum balance for any one site.

In addition to Ufton and Harbury, this calcareous grassland habitat is also found in disused railway cuttings and quarries from Rugby (Ashlawn Cutting, Parkfield Quarry) south-west through Stockton (Stockton Cutting, Nelson's Quarry) to the Kineton area (Goldicote Cutting, Oxhouse Farm Cutting, Lighthorne Heath Quarry). Even as far west as Henley-in-Arden, a railway cutting nature reserve has a good number of lime-rich wild flowers. Species characteristic of this habitat include centaury, yellow-wort, hairy violet, stemless thistle, purging flax and, in the autumn, the deep purple of felwort. Ant-hills abound here too, built by the tiny yellow meadow ant from pincer-fulls of clay excavated from deep underground. Occasionally black meadow ants may be seen in these ant-hills: invaders that have defeated the original builders in battle. Both may also fall prey to the probing beak of the green woodpecker as it searches for its favourite food. Even if the woodpeckers are not seen or heard, evidence of their presence may remain as deep stab marks in the soil, or their droppings which, when dry, crumble to reveal thousands of ant heads. When the ant-hills have been abandoned they still affect the flora of these heavy clay soils, providing a drier habitat for patches of the lemon-coloured mouse-ear hawkweed, whose leaves show the reason for its name. Orchids in these grasslands include common spotted and twayblade with greater butterfly orchid in shadier places and bee orchid rarer. A yellow-lipped version of this bee orchid (var. *chlorantha*) was found at Ufton in 1985, and the wasp orchid – arguably a separate species – has only one good site in Ettington, after a second disappeared under road works at Stretton-on-Fosse. The man orchid is nearing the limits of its British range in Warwickshire, and has only one colony, which appears to be slowly declining.

Such a wealth of wild flowers on lime-rich grasslands inevitably supports a host of butterflies and other invertebrates. In May and June dingy and grizzled skippers are on the wing, with green hairstreak, small blue, and the day-flying moths burnet companion and mother Shipton, the latter named from its fore-wing pattern, allegedly resembling the profile of a wizened old lady. The dramatic black and white of marbled white butterflies are found in this habitat, with narrow bordered fivespot burnet and six spot burnet moths joining them in July in railway cuttings from Newton and Ashlawn to Harbury and Combrook. The dark green fritilliary – now perhaps Warwickshire's only fritillary – is primarily a grassland species in the Gloucestershire Cotswolds. No more than three or four colonies have been recorded for Warwickshire since 1940 and, by the end of the 1970s, only two survived. A lack of sightings since then may mean that it too is extinct in the county, despite having apparently favourable habitats. Wood white butterflies began breeding at two railway cutting sites in the 1970s, but only remained until the early 1980s, when both declined to extinction. In contrast, the Duke of Burgundy butterfly was rediscovered near Halford in a locality where it was last recorded in the 1920s. The insect is dependent on the delicate balance between grassland and scrub, and the degree of shelter given to its larval foodplant, the cowslip. Reasons for such changes are not easily understood, let alone managed.

Over two hundred different species of moths occur in Warwickshire's grasslands, including a number of rarities confined to the limestone, such as the six-belted clearwing, lace border, chalk carpet, brown scallop and ochreous pug: these are species whose main stronghold is in south-east England. One of the blue butterflies, the brown argus, was once present at three or four locations in Warwickshire but is now known from only two: Ministry of Defence land at Kineton and river plain gravel at Charlecote. In the former its larval foodplant is common storksbill, but at the latter dove's-foot cranesbill.

Among the hundreds of other invertebrates, glow-worms stand out, quite literally, at night. The strange greenish glow emitted by the wingless females attracts flying males at local sites from Newbold Quarry and Herald Way Marsh to Oversley Wood and the Grand Union Canal near Long Itchington, as well as at other sites further south. Glow-worm larvae are predators of snails, injecting a fluid which both paralyses the snail and dissolves it: the resulting liquid is then sucked up by the larva.

Lime-rich soils also encourage snails: indeed, few snails can exist in acidic soils because of the lack of calcium for their shells. The banded snail is clearly conspicuous with its brown stripes around a pale yellow shell. The genetics of this snail have been extensively studied, as individuals can be recognised by the different width and pattern of their bands; orange background colours are also found too. A total of over 150 different species of slugs and snails in Warwickshire, compared with the British total of 200, shows the county to be well-represented with these often overlooked invertebrates.

Marbled white butterflies are often found in areas of lime-rich soils. (AP)

61

With all this emphasis on calcareous grasslands, it should be remembered that neutral and acid grasslands have their important species too. Stonebridge Meadows nature reserve, south of Coventry, has harebell, tormentil and field scabious flowering on a grassy hillside, the scabious eaten by the larvae of a beautiful metallic green sawfly(*Abia sericea*). Old colliery spoil heaps too can provide a much-needed refuge for those species able to grow in acidic soils, including wavy hair-grass, common bent-grass, sheep's sorrel, heath bedstraw and tormentil, in sites near Polesworth, Dordon and Baxterley.

Other rare grassland plants are scattered around the county, such as the rediscovered wild tulip near Southam, the drooping star-of-Bethlehem at Alderminster, autumn crocus on Warwick racecourse, autumn lady's tresses in Rugby and the single appearance of St Barnaby's thistle at Ufton Fields.

Mosses abound in grassland, with branched shoots of *Brachythecium* species common everywhere and tiny upright shoots of *Funaria hygrometrica* on bare soil, especially where fires have occurred. As in woodland, there are some species preferring lime rich soils, while others favour the more acid. Fungi too are widespread in grassland, with shaggy inkcap and fairy-ring mushrooms in pastures throughout the county, joined by parasol and field mushrooms where there is animal manure. At Draycote Meadows the short grass in early summer makes it easy to see huge fairy rings, circular patches of lusher grass created by the fungus advancing. Calculations of the rate of growth of these fungal rings show that some circles could be centuries old.

Wherever taller vegetation persists, such as at Wilmcote Rough or the edge of The Belfry golf course, populations of grasshoppers and bush crickets can develop. Sunshine encourages the wing-rubbing 'chirping' of males of common field grasshopper and meadow grasshopper, a behaviour that alerts females to their presence. After mating the eggs are laid in groups just under the soil and hatch after winter into worm-like larvae. These wriggle up to the soil surface and shed their outer cuticle, revealing small 'nymphs' looking just like small wingless adults. Resembling grasshoppers but with long antennae, bush crickets can be heard in warm summer nights from July onwards. The females have a fierce looking ovipositor at the rear of the abdomen, whose sole purpose is to inject eggs into plant stems, where their initial development is protected.

Other grassland plant feeders include shieldbugs, capsids, aphids, wasps and bees, tortoise beetles, weevils and frog hoppers, whose larvae cause the familiar 'cuckoo spit' in grasses and other plants in roadside verges and gardens throughout Warwickshire. Many of these insects then fall prey to carnivorous invertebrates such as damsel bugs, assassin bugs, ground beetles, soldier beetles, ladybirds, longhorn beetles, spiders and harvestmen. Some are parasitized by mites or ichneumon wasps, or fed on by vertebrates, giving hundreds of complex interactions between predator and prey. Conservation management for invertebrates is certainly not an easy subject!

In general, the vertebrates in grassland are influenced more by the physical conditions than by the plant or insect species present. Dry grassland (as in Goldicote Cutting) may support common lizard, a species also found in heathland and certainly not common in

Field mushroom and shaggy inkcap – typical fungi of pastures. (JPW)

62

Wolf spiders are voracious predators of small insects. (WNCT)

Warwickshire. Wet grassland, in contrast (as at Ufton Fields), will favour grass snakes. Birds too have marked preferences based on wetness, with the drier ground holding little more than skylarks. Damp meadows, in winter, support a wide range of birds, such as flocks of lapwing and black-headed gull. Golden plover may also be seen at Wellesbourne airfield or fields at Willoughby, along with jackdaws, rooks and starlings. Redwings and fieldfare will be joined by song thrushes and blackbirds, when the rising water table takes invertebrates nearer the field's surface.

In addition to common lizards, dry grasslands are also the favoured habitat of another Warwickshire lizard, the slow-worm. Disused railway embankments and cuttings seem a prime habitat, but they also occur at Hartshill Hayes, Coleshill Bog, Brandon Wood, Kenilworth Common, Stretton-on-Fosse and in the Alcester area: a total of nine locations for the county.

By far the most common and widespread of the mammals of Warwickshire grassland, the rabbit makes a huge impact by grazing everything it finds palatable. In many nature reserves, including Harbury Spoil Bank and Henley Sidings, rabbits are responsible for keeping the scrub at bay, by nipping out young growing shoots of hawthorn and blackthorn: they can also affect crops. Numbers are kept in check by their predators, including fox, stoat and people. The field vole's entire life depends on grasses: it eats them, makes its nest from them, and constructs a maze of tunnels among their stems and roots. The common shrew is also at home here, its high-pitched squeaking often only detected by those with good hearing. Feeding on insects, it is constantly active and dies if deprived of food for more than a few hours. A third but much less common small mammal is equally at home in this grassland habitat – the harvest mouse. Although traditionally associated with corn fields, it is also found among grass stalks, using its prehensile tail to aid its movement.

Danger is never far away for these last three species, either in the form of attack from above by kestrels and tawny owls, or at ground level by stoats and weasels. Generally keeping to the shelter of scrub or hedges, stoats and weasels feed extensively on mammals, making good use of grassland on the M6 and M42 verges. The larger stoats sometimes hunt in family groups for rabbits, voles and mice but also climb to take birds and eggs. The smaller weasels hunt along mouse and vole tunnels, also taking beetles, birds and eggs. Underground another typical grassland animal, the mole, spends its time checking its tunnels for earthworms and any other invertebrates that have carelessly fallen in. With extremely poor eyes, it relies on smell and vibrations to keep it aware of its surroundings, and uses its immensely powerful fore-limbs to excavate the tunnel system, pushing the unwanted soil above ground to form mole-hills familiar in meadows, especially at Arrow.

When grassland becomes invaded by scrub, the area often deteriorates for wild flowers, as woody species such as hawthorn, blackthorn, elder, rose or willow shade out low-growing plants. At the same time the area may begin to support more bird species, attracted by the greater variety of nesting and roosting sites as well as the autumn feeding. There are some plants that thrive in the lower light conditions, such as spurge laurel under hawthorn on lime-rich soils, at Harbury Spoil Bank, or bilberry under birch on acid soils at Clowes Wood. The first birds of scrub conditions are wren, willow warbler, linnet and yellowhammer, with garden warbler and whitethroat not far behind – the latter particularly where there are patches of gorse.

Grasshopper warblers may also be present, their cricket-like reeling song carrying for a considerable distance from the top of dense bramble scrub or other low bushes in the Tame

Stoats can climb trees, searching for birds and eggs. (JPW)

valley, at Brandon or Ufton Fields. Later in the succession, as the scrub becomes denser and the tree canopy begins to develop, redpoll and turtle dove may move in, although neither are as frequent as in years gone by. Finally, as the scrub matures into woodland, so the birds typical of that habitat arrive: dunnock, blackbird, blackcap, chiffchaff and chaffinch. It is usually at this stage that others, notably linnet, yellowhammer and garden warbler begin to disappear. From the tallest clumps the rattle of a lesser whitethroat or the purring of a turtle dove may be heard, while in one or two favoured spots in the south of the county a nightingale can be heard singing from the densest thickets.

Although it provides many nest sites, scrub is most important for birds in late summer and autumn, when a host of species come to feed on its rich harvest of berries. Mistle thrushes sometimes arrive immediately after breeding to secure their winter food by vigorously defending a territory. Migrant fieldfares, redwings, song thrushes and blackbirds then arrive from October onwards to feed avidly until by the turn of the year most bushes have been stripped bare of berries.

Outside the breeding season, dense thickets of scrub are frequently used for roosting at sites from Kingsbury Water Park to Stockton Cutting, as they provide relative safety and warmth. In addition to the hordes of thrushes that have fed there during the day, huge flocks of wood pigeons, linnets, redpolls, greenfinches, chaffinches, buntings and sparrows arrive every evening to roost. Among the more unusual birds, long-eared owls frequently roost in dense scrub in the more remote parts of the county, often showing a preference for hawthorn, while a great grey shrike might exceptionally be seen on the watch for prey at Ufton Fields or Newbold Comyn.

Scrub has not declined as much in the county as meadows, but both habitats are readily destroyed and often their wildlife importance is simply not appreciated. It is certainly well worth going to look at any of the last remaining hay meadows to remind yourself of the beauty of this almost-lost heritage.

Weasels tend to hunt among the grasses for small mammals. (JPW)

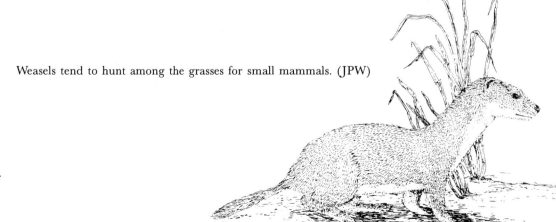

ABOVE: Cowslip meadows are now increasingly uncommon: this one in the south-east of the county was ploughed up in the early 1980s. (JRR) LEFT: Cowslip close-up. (WNCT) RIGHT: Green-veined orchid flourishes with cowslips at Draycote Meadows nature reserve. (AGM)

65

ABOVE: Ufton Fields nature reserve, owned by the County Council and managed by the Trust, is an abandoned limestone quarry. (JB) LEFT: Management at Ufton Fields includes grazing with Jacob's sheep. (MWF) RIGHT: Railway embankments can have a wide range of wild flowers, as at the Trust's Henley Cutting nature reserve. (JRR)

LEFT: Ant hills are a sign of old grassland. (JRR) RIGHT: Ants are preyed on by green woodpeckers. (DRC) BELOW: Binton road verge has had five species of orchids recorded. (JRR) LEFT: Bee orchid, found on Binton verge and many nature reserves on the Lias clays. (JRR)

LEFT: Hoverfly. (JRR). CENTRE: Marbled white butterfly. (JRR)
RIGHT: Common field grasshopper. (CM) BELOW: Slow worm are
found in rough grassland, although not common in the county. (JRR)

ABOVE: Moles feed on the many earthworms under grassland. (FCM)
BELOW: Shelly Green hay meadow in 1982: a mass of heath spotted orchids.

LEFT: Because a hypermarket was to be built on Shelly Green hay meadow, the Trust agreed to move it as a last resort. Contractors cut the 2-acre field to 15cm depth in February 1987. (CET) RIGHT: The ground was so wet turves had to be removed by hand: volunteers and Trust staff helped. (MWF) BELOW: Turves on pallets were moved by tractors. (AT)

LEFT: Loaded onto articulated lorries with fork-lift trucks. (MWF) and RIGHT: transported up the M42 to a receiver site, the turves were laid by hand on the prepared ground. (MWF) BELOW: The result – unfortunately – was a change in species dominance: the meadow is not what it was. (MWF)

Over the Heath

(CBH)

An acre of barren ground, long heath, brown furze

The Tempest

Heathlands have always been associated with barren or 'waste' land, unused by woodsmen and suitable only for poor grazing. They are the lowland equivalents of the moorlands which still extend over large areas of upland Wales and Scotland. In the lowland Midlands, however, this habitat, once so widespread, has been almost entirely destroyed over the last few hundred years. The infertile sandy soils which generally underly heaths, and the poor quality of the grazing, meant that they were prime candidates for agricultural improvement, later followed by housing. Today the majority of heaths in Warwickshire occur only as names of villages or suburbs: Whiteacre Heath, Hockley Heath, Westwood Heath, Stoke Heath, Ryton Heath. The Dunsmore Heath around Rugby is long since vanished and with it the legendary dun cow, whereas Wolford Heath in the deep south of the county is probably the most recently lost.

Heath is characterised by its plants: heather (or 'ling') is often dominant with gorse, broom, bracken and birch. The neater western gorse marks the transition to heath woodland, with heath bedstraw, tormentil and sheep's sorrel among the few flowers to be found. Grasses of heaths include wavy hair-grass, creeping soft-grass, heath grass, mat grass and purple moor-grass. The reason for this characteristic but fairly uniform vegetation is simple: heaths occur on acid soils, and only a few plant species can tolerate high acidity. Centuries of leaching by rainfall have impoverished the sandy soils, removing minerals and nutrients and leading to a habitat of high stress for plants.

Two other factors of critical importance for heaths are grazing and fire. Fire is important because the seeds of many heathland plants are specifically adapted to germinate after a short high temperature, and so flourish after a rapid fire passes through. If fires in Warwickshire seem unlikely, recent research has shown evidence of fires in the pre-historic woodlands of south-west Ireland, and across the world in the United States and in Australia lightning fires are now recognised as important natural phenomena. Perhaps in Warwickshire too the woodlands have not always been damp enough to keep out fire, and heathland has naturally

RIGHT: Field voles are found in most rough grassland and even roadside verges. (RC) BELOW: Green-veined orchids at Draycote Meadows nature reserve — Warwickshire's finest hay meadow. (JRR) LEFT: Skylark — a bird of open grassland. (ML) CENTRE: Small blue butterflies now only have five colonies in Warwickshire. (JRR)

73

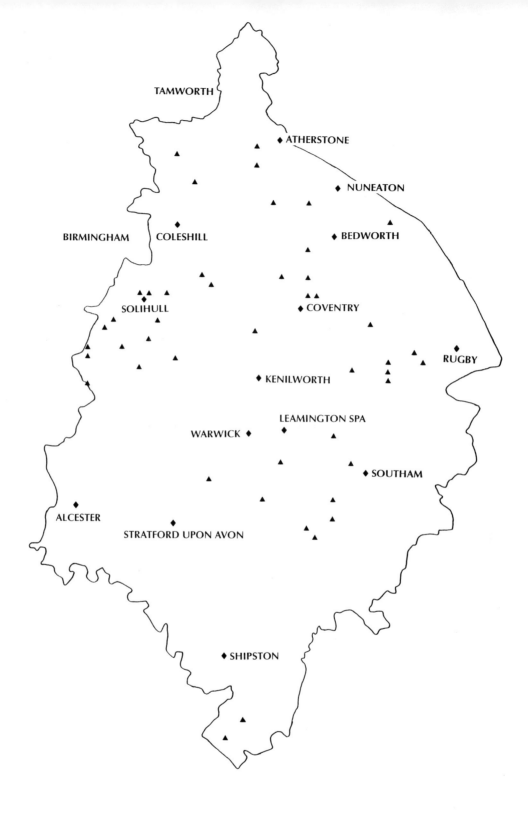

Heathland in Warwickshire. Evidence of place names ending in 'Heath'
△ gives some indication of the extent of heathland in Warwickshire.
Other names not mapped, but implying heathland, are 'moor', 'broom'
and 'furze'. (DRM)

made its mark. Certainly upland moors outside Warwickshire are still managed today by burning, to keep a continual supply of young shoots for grazing. Sutton Park's heathy areas have also sometimes been burnt, but more by accident rather than by design. Grazing by livestock – or once by native animals – is a final key factor determining what happens in heathland. Too much grazing leads towards a dominance by grasses at the expense of the slow-growing heather. Too little grazing and the pioneer seeds of birch soon become established and woodland develops. For heathland to persist over time, all of these factors need to be right, and all need to be maintained.

Although true heathland vegetation contains relatively few species, there is variety provided by topography. Where there is a natural hollow, so water accumulates and a bog develops as at Coleshill Pool, Bickenhill Plantation, and Corley Moor. The most important bog plant is a moss – *Sphagnum* – whose constant growth eventually forms hummocks for other plants to colonise. There are many different species of *Sphagnum*, some needing a microscope to confirm their identification and each with distinct preferences as to degree of wetness and water quality. Bogs are low in nutrients, so the plants occuring here must be adapted by growing only slowly. They decompose even more slowly, forming peat over hundreds of years. Characteristic species of the wetter areas include cottongrass, harestail, rushes and sedges. Purple colour is provided by meadow thistle, lousewort, and cross-leaved heath, with other typical bog plants including bog bean, bog pimpernel, marsh violet, marsh cinquefoil and marsh pennywort, the smallest of the umbellifers. In addition marsh bedstraw, marsh horsetail and devil's-bit scabious add to the diversity of these boggy places.

Few grasses survive the waterlogged conditions but purple moor-grass can because of its specialised root structure, where air-spaces allow the root to continue to respire and grow when others would simply die. Some sedges share this feature, and so occur here too.

A small number of plants of bogs are carnivores, supplementing their usual diet of minerals and water with insects that they catch. Sundew snares small flies and ants on its sticky tentacles and, when the insect dies, secretions from the plant digest it, absorbing its goodness into the leaves. Butterwort too is insectivorous, but here the whole tiny leaf is sticky and acts as a fly-trap, digesting its prey.

The main areas of heathland in Warwickshire used to extend right across the centre of the county, from Sutton Coldfield in the north-west to Rugby in the east, and south wherever the soil conditions allowed. Today the only

Gorse is typical of Warwickshire heaths. (CBH)

remaining sites occur as isolated pockets at Grendon and Baddesley Common, around Coleshill, Corley Moor, and in some areas near Earlswood and Studley: tiny fragments of what used to be. To find a good area of heathland – in fact one of the best in the Midlands – we need to travel outside the current boundary of Warwickshire to Sutton Park.

Sutton Park was a deer park in 1450, with land set aside for woods, for grazing and with heathland too. As the town of Birmingham became a city, and sprawled to the north and west, it merged with Sutton Coldfield and housing now surrounds the Park. By a strange quirk of fate, instead of being built on like so many other deer parks, or simply transformed into arable farmland, Sutton Park still exists today with a unique assemblage of natural habitats: woodland, grassland, pools and heathland.

The plants of Sutton Park include all the species typical of heath: heather, bell heather and gorse, with cross-leaved heath, bogbean, sundew and butterwort in the damper hollows. These

heathland plants support many species of dependent insects, including heath ladybird, green tiger beetle, heath shieldbug and heath damsel bug. Sutton Park was one of the last county localities for the marsh fritillary butterfly, and its larval foodplant – devil's-bit scabious – still occurs among the damp grassland. The green hairstreak butterfly is still found, and in 1988 was observed laying eggs on cranberry in preference to the more abundant bilberry and cowberry. This is a new foodplant for anywhere in England, although there is a record from Scotland dating from the last century. A total of 21 species of butterfly have been recorded in the Park since 1940 but only the green hairstreak, small heath and small copper regularly breed in the heathy areas.

Moths too have a number of heathland dependent species present in the Park. The grey scalloped bar is one of the rarest, its caterpillars feeding on bell-heather or cross-leaved heath. The beautiful yellow underwing is also a heather feeder, and may be seen in rapid flight during hot sunshine in this its only Warwickshire location. Sadly the wood tiger, heath rustic and neglected rustic have not been found in the Park for many years, and are probably extinct in the county. On the positive side, the moth list from the Park still includes a wide range of species, many with drab colours despite their exotic names: the suspected, grass emerald, lead belle, July belle, chevron, northern spinach, scarce tissue, ling pug, narrow-winged pug, grass wave, true lover's knot and barred chestnut. Two larger moths, the fox moth and the emperor, both have caterpillars feeding on heather.

Other rare insects have been recorded from Sutton Park in the last few years, such as two heathland species of hoverfly, *Sphaerophoria philanthus* and *Chrysotoxum arcuatum*. The first of these has also been recorded in heathy areas in Brandon and Oversley Woods, but the latter has not been recorded anywhere in Warwickshire except the Park, and is at the southerly limit of its distribution in Britain.

Sutton Park is also the only locality in the area large enough to support any typically heathland birds; the other fragments of heath are just too small. Even within the Park, the isolation of different habitats and increasing disturbance have led to a steady decline in heathland birds over the years. Nevertheless, the site remains of considerable importance to both breeding and migratory species. Willow warbler and redpoll are typical of light birch scrub, but tree pipit has all but disappeared. Meadow pipits, skylarks and yellowhammers frequent areas of open grassland, heather and gorse, but stonechats and whinchats now only breed erratically. The latter both still pass through in the autumn, together with a few wheatears, all three species being attracted to freshly burnt areas. Whitethroats nest among the gorse, in lower numbers than in the past, and even curlew visit in the summer.

Outside the breeding season there are few birds on the open heath, but small populations of pheasant, grey partridge and red-legged partridge remain among the cover of the heathers. Kestrels and sparrowhawks regularly hunt the area, but it is some years now since a scarcer raptor such as merlin or hen harrier was recorded. The wetter parts of Sutton Park's heath have distinctive birds as well as wild flowers. In the boggy valleys, displaying snipe and 'reeling' grasshopper warblers give interest to a summer's evening, while winter brings a small influx of water rails and perhaps a jack snipe. At dusk woodcock can be seen leaving their bracken-clad roosts and coming to the water's edge to feed.

Whinchats can be seen on migration, but no longer breed in the county.
(CBH)

Altogether Sutton Park remains a jewel in Birmingham's natural treasury, and a reminder to the rest of Warwickshire of what was, until only a short time ago, a widespread habitat, taken for granted. The future management of the Park is critical to its survival, and it is vital that its importance for wildlife is emphasised now, when recreational pressures are so great.

Some of the most characteristic animals of heathlands are the reptiles, basking on the sandy soils to warm up their bodies, and fortunately not solely restricted to Sutton Park. The adder – Britain's only venomous snake – is now rare in Warwickshire, with only two recorded populations. At Clowes Wood the last sightings were in 1985 but the other known site on heathy land near Kenilworth supports a thriving population and, there may be others in suitable areas around Baddesley. Feeding on young birds, frogs, newts and small mammals, adders pose little threat to people, yet are still relentlessly persecuted. The Kenilworth site also maintains populations of grass snake, slow-worm and common lizard – totalling all four of Warwickshire's reptiles.

The common lizard itself is nowhere common in the county with only 16 sites in total. This fast-moving reptile may be seen basking in the sun at Sutton Park, or some of the remaining heaths in north Warwickshire. It is also found in scrub at Goldicote Cutting nature reserve in the south of the county in a similarly dry, warm environment, and a population even survives at Hearsall Common in Coventry, feeding on insects, spiders, and other invertebrates.

Among this picture of declining habitat there is one glimmer of hope, surprisingly related to roads and motorways. Where these have been constructed in areas of sandy soils, and the road verges not smothered with weed-rich topsoil or alien plantings, the beginnings of heathland can now be seen. Gorse is the first coloniser, with broom close behind. Given the right management, heather could follow, and new heathlands begin to flourish. All it needs is the recognition that heathland does have a value and importance: it is not wasteland at all.

Lizards can still be found on dry grassy banks on heaths and rough ground. (CBH)

ABOVE: Sutton Park – the greatest remaining heathland in the region. (JV & GRH) BELOW: Little
Bracebridge Pool is one of many open water areas in the Park. (JV & GRH)

ABOVE: Heath spotted orchid. (WNCT) CENTRE: The small insectivorous plant, sundew, traps insects on its sticky tentacles. (JRR) BELOW: Bog pimpernel is another tiny plant of boggy areas. (JRR) RIGHT: Birch scrub soon establishes on ungrazed heath. (JRR)

79

OPPOSITE ABOVE LEFT: Small copper butterflies thrive on heaths and in rough grassland wherever their larval foodplant – sorrel – is found. (CM) CENTRE: Emperor moths are the most spectacular heathland insects. (JRR) BELOW: Emperor moth caterpillars feed only on heather. (JRR) ABOVE RIGHT: Stonechats are typical of heathland, but no longer breed in the county. (ML) CENTRE: Dry heaths and banks encourage lizards. (CM) BELOW: Slow-worms also occur in heathy areas. (JRR)

ABOVE: Grendon Heath, one of the few surviving heathy areas in Warwickshire. (JRR) LEFT: Crossleaved heath thrives in damp hollows and bogs. (JRR) CENTRE: Green hairstreak butterflies are found in heaths and in lime-rich grasslands. (JRR) RIGHT: Adder are typical of heathland and some still survive in the county. (JRR)

Brandon Marsh. (AGM)

Waters and Wetland

There is a willow grows aslant a brook,
That shows his hoar leaves in the glassy stream

(CBH)

Hamlet, Prince of Denmark

Some twelve thousand years ago, as the last Ice Age relented, melting glaciers would have provided Warwickshire with large areas of water in lakes, pools, rivers and marshes. Today there are no large natural lakes, few marshes, the rivers have been dredged and the water table has been lowered for the better existence of humans and their crops. Although the willow still grows aslant the brook, the stream may now be a metre below its natural depth.

Waters and wetland occur in three distinct habitats in Warwickshire – open water, including lakes and ponds, marshes, and flowing water in rivers and streams. Much of the open water occurs as a direct result of our needs in other areas: reservoirs for water supply; flooded land after quarrying or mining subsidence; canals once for transport; old mill pools or fish ponds created for needs of former times. Marshes, where water meets the land, occur around many of these lakes and ponds, as well as alongside the slower stretches of rivers. The third distinct wetland habitat of rivers and streams have been drastically altered over the years, straightened and deepened and even culverted under our towns.

Some of the older lakes, in deer parks and private estates, look almost natural despite their artificial origins. Lakes like this occur at Sutton Park, Seeswood Pool, Packington Park, Coombe Abbey, Wootton Wawen and Compton Verney. To these have been added larger reservoirs at Draycote and Shustoke, smaller reservoirs at Oldbury, Earlswood, Napton and Wormleighton, mining subsidence pools at Alvecote and Bedworth, and gravel quarry lakes from Brandon Marsh on the Avon to Kingsbury Water Park on the Tame. Abandoned limestone workings have also created many smaller pools, from Newbold north of Rugby, south-west through Stockton and Ufton, to Long Itchington and Bishops Itchington. Some villages like Idlicote and Long Itchington still retain a village pond.

In these lakes and pools the main plant of open water is the yellow water lily, with a subtle scent sometimes likened to brandy, and brandy bottle-shaped fruiting heads. Amphibious bistort is also common, along with the more subdued flowers of broad-leaved and curled pondweed, mare's-tail, reed canary grass and Canadian waterweed. This last species, introduced from North America, is now found throughout Britain, although rarely producing its white, surface flowers. The tiny floating duckweeds are widespread on the smaller pools, together with water starwort and another introduced bu naturalised plant, the minute water

83

ABOVE: Reedbed and open water at Alvecote Pools nature reserve. (JRR) RIGHT: Yellow flag thrives in marshes and pond margins throughout the county. (JRR) CENTRE: The banded demoiselle damselfly breeds in cleaner waters of the River Blythe and upper Avon. (FCM) BELOW: Coventry Canal. (CMT) RIGHT: Kingfisher caught feeding at Brandon Marsh nature reserve. (RC)

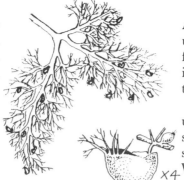

fern *Azolla*. This species, also native to America, can form complete carpets over small ponds, turning from a bluish green to a deep red in autumn. Frosts soon kill it, however, and so its dominance is usually short-lived.

A less common species in pools is the carnivorous plant, greater bladderwort. This thrives in one of the lakes at Alvecote pools, with its tiny underwater bladders serving as final prison cells for hapless invertebrates, which then add to the plant's mineral needs.

Water soldier is another uncommon plant, rising to the surface to flower during the summer in lakes such as in Wedgnock Old Park, and sinking safely to the bottom each winter.

These open water plants have no need of roots, as they absorb all the minerals they need directly from the water. Indeed, roots could prove a liability in depths over a few metres, particularly when water levels fluctuate. Hardly surprising then that few species are found in the open water, compared with the huge diversity at the water's edge.

Probably the most visible insects of Warwickshire's lakes and ponds are the dragonflies and damselflies. These two groups are easily distinguished by their size, and by the way they hold their wings at rest: dragonflies remain with their wings outstretched, but damselflies fold them over their backs. A total of 19 species now breed in the county (out of a total for Britain of 38), all with complex life histories involving adults flying and hunting in the air, and larvae swimming and hunting underwater. Good sites include Kingsbury Water Park, Brandon Marsh, Pagets Lane Pool and Ufton Fields: all places with a diversity of pools, marsh and grassland.

Many damselflies of still waters have pale blue and black abdomens, species being distinguished by the pattern of these colours. Three of the most widespread species are the blue-tailed, azure, and common blue damselflies, which may be seen flying over small pools and marshes from May to September. Males and females link together during mating and often fly in tandem, egg-layer over water or among pond-side vegetation. Their larvae, which take a year or two to reach maturity, can be recognised by three leaf-like gills at the end of the abdomen. The white-legged damselfly, scarce nationally, can be seen regularly at Stockton Cutting Nature Reserve.

Dragonflies can readily be divided into two groups: hawkers and darters. The southern hawker is one of the most common hawkers, with a dramatic black, blue and green body, and a swift and agile flight as it hunts and catches its prey on the wing. Its larva or nymph is a drab brown, spending two years below the water eating anything that it can capture with its 'mask' – an extendable set of pincers on its lower jaw. Darters are named because of their habit of darting out after a passing insect, then returning to a favourite perch. One of the most common is the broad-bodied chaser which inhabits ponds and slow-moving water throughout the county. The broad abdomen is chalky blue in mature males, but brown in younger males and females. The nymphs have a similar lifestyle to the southern hawker, but are more sedentary, burying themselves in the mud and waiting for the prey to come to them.

Under the water there is as much diversity of life as above it. Hundreds of complex food chains begin with the simplest forms of plant life – the algae. These microscopic species are often forgotten when studying pond life, yet without their presence the majority of life in ponds and lakes could not survive. Collectively called phytoplankton, the algae float within the water body, maintaining their position by means of tiny oil droplets in their cells or by an increased surface area with elaborate spines. Algae represent an enormous range of plant life, from green algae (related to higher plants) through the golden-yellow diatoms and desmids (with no land-living relatives) to the blue-greens. These latter organisms, although commonly called algae, have extremely simple cell structures, much more closely related to bacteria than the rest of

After emerging as adults, dragonflies spend some minutes waiting for
their wings to expand and harden. (SDA)

the algae. Each of these types of organism is competing for the limited minerals
and nutrients in the water, growing and dividing as fast as resources allow. From
time to time a certain combination of water chemistry and temperature can
trigger huge 'blooms' – population explosions of one particular species. These
can kill fish by using up all the oxygen in the water, and some species of blue-
greens also give off toxic byproducts which can poison fish and mammals alike.
Smaller blooms are quite common on most open waters, including Alvecote Pools,
Earlswood Lakes, Draycote Reservoir and New Waters in Warwick.

Feeding on these algae is an army of microscopic animals – the zooplankton.
These include single-celled organisms as well as minute invertebrates such as the
water flea *Daphnia*. Another common species, *Cyclops*, has a single light-sensitive
'eye' at the top of its head, and tows clusters of eggs around as it swims with a
jerky motion through the pond. Larger animals feed on smaller animals,
producing food webs of great complexity, even in a humble garden pond. Three-spined
sticklebacks are common more or less county wide, feeding on *Daphnia* and *Cyclops*. During the
breeding season males become flushed with a red colour, and attract females into specially
constructed nest areas, where the eggs are laid. Adults may be preyed upon by larger fish or
birds, or simply parasitised by the fish louse. *Daphnia* and *Cyclops* are also food for tadpoles of
frogs and newts, as well as larvae of all sorts of insects. As the zooplankton and phytoplankton
die, their remains float down to the bottom of the pond, accumulating with dead and decaying
plant remains. This material then becomes food for many detritus-feeders such as the water
hog louse crawling over the bottom, bright red bloodworms (or midge larvae), filter-feeding
pea-shell cockles, or armour-plated ostracods. Another source of food – the flowering plants
of the water's edge – is exploited by snails, two of the most conspicuous being the great
ramshorn and great pond snail. Leeches feed on these snails and other invertebrates too,
although they often cause unnecessary alarm to pond-dippers as well.

Apart from dragonfly nymphs, still water is home for other voracious insects too: the
common backswimmer, which pierces its prey; the water scorpion with powerful pincer-like
forelegs, and the great diving beetle which swims strongly to attack everything it can. Each
of these insects needs to breathe oxygen from the air, and each has different ways of doing so:
the backswimmer traps air in hairs on its body; the water scorpion has a long snorkel-like tube
at the end of its abdomen; and the diving beetle traps air under its wing-cases. With all these
predators about it is not surprising that good defences are needed too. Snails have an obvious
protection, but many caddis fly larvae make their own cases from stones or twigs, and then
carry them round as they crawl on the mud surface. Other common invertebrates of ponds
include water lice, feeding on detritus; water mites and water spiders; mosquito and midge
larvae; and mayfly larvae, whose adults emerge to breed yet live for just a day or two.
Freshwater crayfish are not common and generally occur in lime-rich rivers and lakes of the
south of England, but thriving populations occur in Coventry Canal and a disused clay pit in
Nuneaton.

For tadpoles entering this crowded and hostile environment, their only protection is their
numbers, the main principle being that enough spawn is laid to ensure that a few survive to

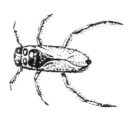

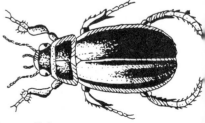

Predators of the shallows: backswimmer, water boatman and great diving
beetle. (WNCT)

breeding age. There are four species of native amphibian in Warwickshire: common frog, common toad, smooth newt, and great crested newt. Unsubstantiated records also exist for the palmate newt, which could live in the acid pools of Sutton Park. The common frog survives well, primarily in garden ponds now that so many ponds in the countryside have ceased to be functional and been filled in. The common toad is also found throughout the county, but it needs large ponds with a depth of about one metre for breeding, and it is declining in numbers as its habitat declines. Adult toads can live much further from water than frogs because they are not dependent on most skin surface for respiration.

Smooth newt records show an apparent decline but, as many garden ponds are now home for these attractive creatures, the real picture may not be so bad. In contrast, the great crested newt has undergone a considerable decline both nationally and internationally over the last few decades. The species is now considered vulnerable within the British Isles, and was given full legal protection under the 1981 Wildlife and Countryside Act. The species only occurs in Europe, and recent studies suggest that the British form may be a different subspecies. The Midlands is currently a stronghold for this threatened amphibian, and populations in Warwickshire remain healthy. They prefer weedy ponds, and will breed only if the water depth is greater than about 50cm. The larvae are highly susceptible to predation by fish, which makes many garden ponds unsuitable but nevertheless there are over twenty breeding sites within Coventry alone. Because of their protected status, it is illegal to touch, catch or interfere with the species or its habitat without a licence from the Nature Conservancy Council.

The only Warwickshire reptile with aquatic tendencies is the grass snake, readily identified by its yellow or cream collar over an olive-green body with darker blotches down each side. By far the most widespread reptile in the county, it is found in any habitat near to water, where it preys on fish and amphibians. It will also invade garden ponds for the frogs there! Laying 20 or so soft-shelled eggs in rotting vegetation, it uses the heat from decomposition to keep the eggs warm. In gardens, compost heaps are a favoured location for these harmless and beautiful creatures.

Whether small pond or large lake, birds are attracted to water, and the larger the lake the greater the list of species using it. The four prime sites in the county for these birds of open water are Alvecote Pools, The Tame valley complex, Brandon marsh on the Avon and Draycote Water. All are artificial lakes, the first three the legacy from mining or quarrying, with Draycote a man-made reservoir. The Tame valley complex, from Tamworth south through Kingsbury Water Park, Coton and Lea Marston pools, the West Midlands Bird Club's reserve at Ladywalk, and the Trust's reserve at Whitacre Heath, forms a series of related lakes and wetland, now becoming of international importance.

Common tern breed in the Tame valley. (WNCT)

Great crested grebe breed on lakes in both Tame and Avon valleys. (HC)

Great crested grebe breeding 'ceremony' includes 'greeting', head shaking and passing weed to each other. (MJ)

Here the breeding birds include such unlikely species as the typical seaside quartet of shelduck, oystercatcher, ringed plover and common tern. Indeed, a thriving colony of common terns annually produce some 40 young. Other more expected wildfowl include great crested and little grebes, teal, gadwall, shoveler and occasionally garganey, pochard, and ruddy duck. Little ringed plover, redshank, snipe, as well as reed, sedge and grasshopper warblers complete an impressive wetland breeding community. Following the breeding season, a large herd of mute swans gather to moult at Alvecote Pools, whence they later disperse down the Tame valley. Large flocks of Canada geese also form, and there is a resident flock of feral greylag geese, which sometimes attracts both pink-footed and white-fronted geese too.

As winter approaches, so wildfowl numbers in the Tame valley increase. Influxes of mallard, teal, shoveler, coot, tufted duck, and pochard arrive to swell the ranks of resident birds, while parties of wigeon and goldeneye add further diversity. Goosander are never numerous or widespread in Warwickshire, but a few are seen in most years. In recent winters huge numbers of diving duck, particularly pochard, have congregated at Lea Marston, often with a few scaup too. Regular watching has also added an impressive list of rarities, including three divers of northern Scotland, the black-throated, red-throated and great northern divers, as well as black-necked and Slavonian grebes, ferruginous duck, common and velvets coters, and long-tailed duck. Cormorants too are regularly noted in the Tame valley, about as far as it is possible to get from their normal coastal cliffs. Gulls are a winter attraction, with large numbers of black-headed, herring and lesser black-backed gulls coming into various roosts. Among them there is always the chance of finding a rarity like Mediterranean, glaucous, or Iceland gull.

Similar birds occur in winter at Brandon Marsh and Draycote Water, though the latter tends to be better for diving duck and the former for dabbling species. Teal especially flock to the specially created pools at Brandon. At Draycote, in addition to the flocks of wigeon that graze the shoreline, good numbers of great crested grebes and a few smew are seen in most winters. Divers too are more regular here then anywhere, despite the disturbance from boats and fishers, and the enormous gull roost regularly holds one or two rarities.

Little ringed plover breeds in the Tame valley.

Shovelers nest in grass and rushes near water. (WNCT)

In spring, once the winter wildfowl have left for their northern breeding grounds, attention turns to waders. If the weather has been mild some, such as snipe, will have been present all winter; in the Tame valley a few redshank, curlew and green sandpiper will have over-wintered too. But in the main it is March before the first little ringed plovers, dunlin, redshank and curlew pass through on their way north. They are followed by the first common sandpipers in April and passage usually peaks in early May, when there are often a few sanderlings along with almost anything else. Whether the passage of waders is good or not depends very much on water levels and weather. In a poor year most birds either bypass the area or simply overfly it without stopping, but in a good year all sorts of exciting birds may pause briefly to the delight of their observers.

Spring can also be a good time for terns and herons. Arctic terns regularly pass through in early May and, if weather conditions force them to come down, their numbers can be impressive. A few sandwich and little terns are also seen in most years, parties of black terns often appear in light easterly winds, and there is always the possibility of a rarer tern. Grey herons can be seen at any time, standing like sentinels on the watch for their next meal of fish or frog. In warm southerly winds a rarer heron, spoonbill or egret may even appear.

By July waders begin to reappear on their return southwards. Green and common sandpipers are always prominent among the early arrivals, particularly at Brandon and Kingsbury. They are quickly followed by the first dunlin, ruff and greenshank, and in August the passage reaches its peak. The spring passage of terns is repeated in the autumn, except the birds may linger longer on their return, feeding for days or even weeks. September usually brings one or two little stints and in good years maybe a few curlew sandpipers, neither seen often in the spring. The first gales of autumn drive a few seabirds inland, with Manx shearwaters and shags appearing first although gannet, Leach's petrel, storm petrel, skua and Sabine's gull have all been noted over the years. Draycote is the most likely place to find these rare vagrants.

Most of the passage waders have left by October, although dunlin may stay longer. At this time a grey plover or storm-driven grey phalarope might be seen, and flocks of wintering snipe start to build up. A few jack snipe usually accompany these early arrivals but seldom stay long, and remain secretive. Water rails are not so elusive and at least some will stay throughout winter if the ground remains unfrozen.

In contrast to this magnificent abundance of birds, there are few mammals of open water. Water shrews are little seen as they are mainly nocturnal, feeding on insects, small fish and even frogs. They are readily identified by their pointed snout and black upperparts. Water voles feed mainly on grass, swimming strongly and hiding in their waterside tunnels on the banks of lakes, rivers and canals. The brown rat looks generally similar, but has a more pointed face and larger ears. The otter was once found in many rivers in the county but is now gone, probably because of disturbance to its wetland habitat. In its place the introduced mink, escaped from captivity, is spreading unchecked and now likely to be seen anywhere in the county. Feeding on fish, small mammals and birds, it can have a disastrous effect locally on bird populations.

Where water meets land so marshes can develop. Marshes occur in low-lying field corners, around ponds, as at Deppers Bridge and Hillmorton, at Bedworth Slough and Ladywalk nature reserve; in woodlands at Temple Balsall and Whichford Wood; and at the edges of rivers, streams, and canals. All these places share in common this combination of water and fertile mud which encourages a host of wild flowers, both beautiful and useful, providing food for insects and shelter for birds.

Colour is provided by yellow flag, marsh marigold, brooklime, water mint, marsh woundwort, common skullcap, and huge drifts of hairy willowherb. White contrasts come from common water crowfoot, gipsywort and wild angelica. In deeper water, the tall pink flowers of flowering rush grow almost surprisingly from the dull reed-like leaves. Sharp eyes will spot the occasional crinkled leaves of sweet flag, whose use in times past as a floor covering provided possibly the first natural air-freshener: when crushed the leaves give off a pleasantly sweet orangey scent. Also used in bygone times were species like soft rush (for rudimentary candles), common reed (thatching and floor-covering), and reed sweet-grass (fodder). Reedmace produces large stands, although its close relative, lesser reedmace, is much less common. Both of these species are often mistakenly called bulrush, allegedly after the Victorian painting 'Moses in the Bulrushes', where the plants illustrated were in fact reedmace. The true bulrush has a much less spectacular flower head, but thick soft stems that were used extensively for rush mats. The diversity of these all-green species is increased with jointed rush, branched bur-reed, water horsetail, and lesser pond sedge: all large plants, not so difficult to identify once their characteristics are known, and are to be found in Warwickshire marshes.

Less common plants of marshes include marsh valerian in the north-west of the county, alternate-leaved golden saxifrage at Temple Balsall and Whichford Wood, and common butterbur, which is nowhere common but forms extensive stands in the shade at Temple Balsall. Southern marsh orchids and they hybrids form splashes of pink colours at Whitacre Heath, Kingsbury and Heral Way Marsh, as well as in isolated fields at Hillmorton and Deppers Bridge. Rarest however, must be the single colony of marsh helleborine recently discovered at Ladywalk nature reserve.

Much smaller is common mudwort, creeping among plants like spike rush at Earlswood Lakes, or water marshwort at Seeswood Pool. Even closer to the mud is fat duckweed at Old Milverton Pool. Bradnocks Marsh, and the Cathiron Canal arm. Shoreweed was confirmed at its only Warwickshire site at Olton reservoir in 1983, in a project organised by Warwickshire Museum, aimed at rediscovering the county's rarest plants. Amid all these plants of the water's edge one is distinctly unwelcome: swamp stonecrop is native to New Zealand, but its recent introduction to Britain has led to it taking over some ponds: another reminder that species introductions can have unpredictable and unwelcome side effects. A strange species for Warwickshire is sea club-rush, recorded at Southam and Flecknoe, where underground salt deposits give rise to saline springs.

Many mosses favour the damp conditions of marshes, as do some fungi such as the yellow swamp russula, and wax caps which grow on *Sphagnum*. However, the huge diversity of wetland plants is dwarfed by the diversity of insects and other invertebrates that they support. Many are specific to one species of plant, but some will happily feed on many, and others simply feed on each other. Some examples of each will give a general picture of these complex inter-relations.

Of the wainscot moths, whose caterpillars are mainly specific to common reed, the southern wainscot was first recorded for the county in 1970. Since then a further two sites in the south-west have been added. Its close relative, the delightfully-named obscure wainscot, is local nationally in the south and east of England, but has two records for Charlecote in 1979 and 1984. Like many of these obscure or difficult-to-identify species, the absence of recorders makes getting complete records a difficult problem. Another relative, the bulrush wainscot, has caterpillars that bore in the stems, not of bulrush,

Marshland grasses include tufted hair-grass, reedmace, wood small-reed
and reed canary grass. (MJ)

90

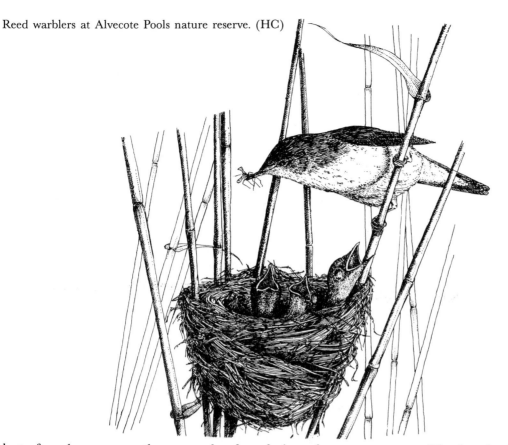

but of reedmace – another example of confusion of common names. The females have the ability to detect reedmace stems from all the other wetland plants, and specialised spines to perforate the stem, levering it apart just enough to lay an egg inside. Another widespread moth is the attractive gold spot, whose larvae have broader tastes, feeding on yellow flag, bur-reed, sedges or even some grasses.

Several of the pools at Sutton Park are particularly important for rare insects, possibly because of their long history as water bodies. Little Bracebridge Pool supports a leaf beetle (*Donacia obscura*) whose larvae feed on aquatic plants, and adults are found at water level on sedges and rushes. Over the whole of Britain this beetle is classified as 'vulnerable' in the Red Data Book for insects, occurring mainly in the uplands of Scotland, yet it has a healthy population in Sutton Park. Other rare insects occurring in good numbers in the Park, but usually found in upland Britain, include a sawfly (*Dolerus bimaculatus*) which feeds on horsetails and a black and orange hoverfly (*Platycheirus perpallidus*).

The typical marshland plants of reedmace, common reed, reed sweet-grass and reed canary-grass provide the ideal nesting habitat for many wetland birds. Reed and sedge warblers and reed bunting are probably the most typical, nesting among willowherb or meadowsweet as well as the predicted common reed. Both warblers are subject to the unwelcome attentions of the cuckoo, although the reed warblers seem favoured. Whitethroats and linnets prefer slightly drier habitats, and so can be found further from water. Wagtails are attracted to marshy areas, yellow wagtail often roosting in reed beds outside the breeding season. Pied wagtail are also widespread in the county, roosting not only in reed beds but also in factories: in a record roost at the Courtauld factory in Coventry, 1,943 birds were counted on 1 January 1971. By late summer swallows and martins may form huge roosts in suitable reed or sallow beds, often attracting a passing hobby. Bedworth Slough used to be particularly favoured, with autumn roots of over 20,000 in the sixties and early seventies. Similar size roosts were also recorded

occasionally at Baginton and Alvecote, but the national decline of the species has led to much smaller roosts recently. Swifts too share the airborne insect feast over lakes and marshes, but also feed more widely over towns and countryside. Their biggest gathering in the Midlands, of over 10,000 was recorded from Draycote Water in May 1975. With so many birds, marshes also attract raptors such as hobby, kestrel, sparrowhawk and merlin, with even the occasional marsh harrier, hen harrier and short-eared owl, in the Avon and Tame valleys. In most winters the extensive stands of common reed at Brandon attract bearded tits, while in a hard winter even a bittern might appear in search of food.

The county's rivers and streams are now less attractive to wildlife than in former years, due to changes in their management as well as changes to the land surrounding them. River corridor management is now more sensitive to the river's ecology than twenty years ago, but to meet human demands rivers are still widened, deepened, and straightened, resulting in significant loss of habitat.

The wildlife of rivers and streams depends on factors such as the underlying rocks, the speed of flow, and the depth of water. Where large rivers flow deep and slow, such as along sections of the Tame, Anker, Avon and Leam, plants and animals of ponds and lakes will be found including purple loose-strife, coot and water vole. In contrast, along small brooks and ditches the vegetation may be that of marshland. In between are the streams and small rivers, surrounded by branched bur-reed, arrowhead, and common water-plantain, with leaves of pond weeds and water crowfoots crowding the channel.

Streams and rivers are also home to water chickweed, water forgetmenot, common fleabane and the poisonous hemlock, with less common species such as the fine-leaved water-dropwort on the River Leam at Birdingbury, tubular water-dropwort on the Blythe near Henley-in-Arden, and small teasel on the Arrow at Coughton.

Invertebrates of streams and rivers show different sensitivities to pollution, and so the presence of different species can be used to indicate water quality. Unpolluted streams can support stoneflies and freshwater shrimps as well as larvae of caseless caddisfly, mayfly and beetles. Pollution, usually from sewage treatment works, reduces oxygen supply and may restrict the invertebrates to blood worms, sludge worms and rat-tail maggots, with sewage fungus in abundance. Plants also show some differences, with river water crowfoot in clean waters but fennel pondweed and blanketweed typical of moderately polluted water.

Within the county the major river catchments, the Tame and the Avon, have suffered differently over the years. The Tame, draining Birmingham and the Black Country, became little more than an open sewer during the Industrial Revolution, with all life extinguished. A landowner at Hams Hall began legal action against Birmingham in 1854, because 'the River Tame . . . which had been noted for its crystal clearness and for the trout which abounded in it, was horribly polluted by the noxious fluids draining into it'. Pollution was not only from domestic waste but also from the many metal industries in the West Midlands, with their various chemical cleaning wastes. A hundred years later, to improve the water quality lower down the river, a series of settlement lakes were planned in the Lea Marston and Kingsbury area. However, before they were built, water quality had improved, and many additional gravel pit lakes had also been made, so the planned series of lakes was reduced. Fish now present in the river include pike, mirror and common carp, chub, dace, roach, tench and gudgeon, although trout are still some way off. Both the Cole and the Blythe joint the Tame at Hams Hall, the Blythe being one of the few rivers in Britain designated a Site of Special Scientific

Interest, because of the variety of habitats along its largely unspoiled length. Trout, barbel and minnow are found in the Blythe, with banded demoiselle and beautiful demoiselle flying over it, all indicators of its cleaner waters.

The River Avon, in contrast, has had much less industrial pollution, although the Sherbourne and Sowe, draining Coventry, have caused concern from time to time. The main pollution problems here are caused by domestic sewage, with Rugby, Coventry, Warwick and Stratford all discharging their treated wastes into the river. In the late 1970s a different problem arose when a Higher Avon Navigation Trust was set up to make the river navigable from Stratford to Warwick. This would have necessitated major engineering and dredging works, and would have removed many of the river's vital shallows and riffles, reducing the diversity of plants, invertebrates, fish and birds. Eventually the proposals went to the House of Lords as a Private Member's Bill, but strong opposition from many individuals and groups, including the Trust, eventually led to it being withdrawn. However, the threat still remains to this tranquil and unspoiled stretch of river, habitat for over 200 species of plants.

Few of Warwickshire's rivers are fast enough for the dipper, a bird of upland streams and rushing water, but it just hangs on in the upper reaches of the Alne and Stour. Grey wagtails also prefer fast-flowing rivers, regularly nesting along the Arrow and the Alne. Kingfishers are to be seen on most rivers, a blue and orange flash as they fly by. Feeding on bullheads, minnows, and tadpoles, they also need riverbanks for their nest holes. Herons too can be found almost anywhere, with moorhen and coot where river flow is slow. The story of the Avon's most treasured bird, the mute swan, will be touched on later.

So from Shakespeare's willow growing aslant a brook to Shakespeare's Avon, the wetlands of Warwickshire continue to support a vital diversity of wildlife. The nature of wetlands has changed over the years, but the many recently created lakes and marshes mean that on balance wetlands have not suffered as much as other habitats.

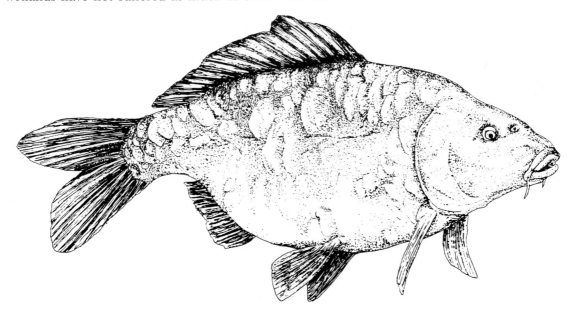

Mirror carp from Kingsbury Water Park. (JPW)

ABOVE: Brandon Marsh nature reserve has developed in old sand and gravel workings in the Avon valley. (WNCT) BELOW: The River Avon between Warwick and Stratford has many shallow riffles like this one at Barford (JV & GRH) OPPOSITE ABOVE: Whitacre Heath nature reserve totals over 100 acres, all now owned by the Trust. (KW) BELOW: Kingsbury Water Park is a County Council Country Park with its own nature reserve. (JV & GRH)

95

ABOVE LEFT: Ragged robin. (KR) CENTRE: Fox sedge. (JRR)
RIGHT: Southern hawker dragonfly. (JSR) CENTRE LEFT: Azure
damselfly. (CM) RIGHT: Adult mayflies only live for a day or two.
(FCM) BELOW LEFT: Backswimmer under the water surface. (JSR)
RIGHT: Great diving beetle. (JSR)

96

ABOVE: The heronry at Coombe Abbey is one of only half a dozen in
the country. (FCM) LEFT: Great crested grebe breed in many lakes in
the Avon and Tame valleys. (AGM) RIGHT: Little grebe do too. (AGM)

ABOVE LEFT: Little ringed plover are uncommon but have bred in the Tame valley. (RC) RIGHT: Water rail at Brandon Marsh. (JSR) CENTRE: Bearded tits thrive at Brandon Marsh. (CM) BELOW: Mating toads need ponds at least 1m deep. (JRR) RIGHT: Water voles are not often seen, but are quite widespread. (CM)

ABOVE LEFT: Grass snake hunt in wet marshes for frogs and newts. (AW) RIGHT: Minnows, found in cleaner waters. (RC) CENTRE: Perch. (FCM) BELOW: and roach, both common in large rivers of the county. (FCM) RIGHT: The River Blythe SSSI meanders peacefully through Solihull. (JRR)

The River Leam at Offchurch. (JAB)

Life on the Farm

(CBH)

Her fallow leas
The darnel, hemlock, and rank fumitory
Doth root upon, while the coulter rusts,
That should deracinate such savagery

King Henry V

Although the fallow fields of Shakespeare's time are no longer with us, more than 80 per cent of the area of Warwickshire, Coventry and Solihull is still farmland, with arable crops dominant, particularly in the south and east, and dairy and mixed farming in the north and west. The coulter (or plough) is certainly not rusty, either in the arable areas or in today's grassland – the two main habitats present on the farm.

In 1887 the agricultural census for the old county of Warwickshire showed over 120,000 acres of grassland, whereas in 1987 the figure for the new county was nearly 160,000. These figures are a little deceptive, however, because grassland quality has changed considerably. A hundred years ago the grass would have been a mixture of pasture (grazed all or most of the year) and hay meadows (cut for hay every July). Today short-term 'leys' predominate, where the land is ploughed up and re-seeded with productive strains of ryegrass. Cowslip meadows, and the Fosse Way have been lost in this way. These leys respond well to added fertiliser, growing more grass than was possible under the old systems. The grass is either eaten by livestock in the field, or cut periodically throughout the summer, to be fermented into silage for later feeding. Such a production system relies heavily on the inputs of fertiliser, especially nitrogen, as well as herbicides to kill off any weeds. These intensively managed grass fields are almost as poor for wildlife as arable land. Gradually ley is invaded by other grasses and even broadleaved species but then it is ploughed up to start again.

Permanent pasture remains unploughed from year to year. In some cases it may be extremely old, with the medieval ridge-and-furrow still noticeable, possibly going back to the Black Death times of the mid-1300s, seen in many fields in the south-east from Shipston-on-Stour and Kineton up to Cosford and Churchover. However, such land has often been improved by top dressing with fertilisers and spraying with herbicides. Usually it is less intensively managed than leys, and so can provide breeding places for species such as skylark and lapwing. Plants present vary with soil type, drainage, and the level of grazing, but might include red and white clovers, creeping thistle, ribwort plantain, creeping buttercup,

Typical pasture grasses: ryegrass, Yorkshire fog, red fescue and cocksfoot. (CBH)

dandelion, cut-leaved cranesbill and common mouse-ear. In addition to the ubiquitous ryegrass, permanent pasture usually also supports other grasses: cocksfoot, red fescue, annual meadow grass and crested dog's-tail. When pastures are over-grazed, particularly by horses, in the Dorridge, Hockley Heath and Balsall Common areas, other species invade, such as curled dock, broad-leaved dock, spear thistle and ragwort. All these plants surviving in grassland are adapted to life in closely grazed pastures in a number of ways: by having their growing shoots protected with spines (thistles) or hidden at the soil surface (plantain); by containing unpalatable or poisonous chemicals (ragwort and dock); or by producing many fast-growing seeds (annual meadow-grass). It is now rare in Warwickshire today to find unimproved permanent pasture managed as it was in bygone times, although the odd few fields still survive near Rowington, Kineton and Combrook, with lady's smock in damper hollows and cowslip in the spring.

Livestock grazing these pastures provides the raw material for a whole series of food chains: dung. Apart from the golden yellow dung flies that lay their eggs on cowpats to provide a ready source of food for their developing larvae, dung beetles too make use of the valuable resource. The largest of these, the metallic dark green or purple dor beetle, digs burrows under dung and forms dung pellets which it transports down tunnels, before laying an egg in each one. The developing larva thus has an individual food supply as well as in-built protection.

Arable farming, where the land is ploughed and crops planted, has been a key part of Warwickshire's growth for at least two thousand years. The lands of the Feldon were largely cleared before Roman times, allowing intensive crop production by the sustainable methods developed and perfected in medieval times. At first sight, therefore, the area of arable farming in Warwickshire has changed little over a long period. What has changed significantly, particularly over the last fifty years, is the way this arable land is managed. A hundred years ago the traditional three- or four-part rotation of crops had been going on for centuries, with barley one year followed by beans, peas or clover the next, wheat in the third year and the fourth left fallow. This rotation system allowed many natural processes to occur: the legume crops of peas and beans added nitrogen to the soil naturally; cattle grazing the fallow or clover added their manure; and the continual presence of each different land-use allowed a variety of wild plants and animals to co-exist.

The mechanisation of arable farming, the invention of an increasingly sophisticated armoury of chemicals and our ignorance of ecological processes has changed this traditional and sustainable system out of all recognition. Instead of recycling soil nutrients we now add

OPPOSITE ABOVE: Dor beetles depend on dung, burrowing under cow-pats to provide food for their larvae. (DS)

102

large amounts of artificial fertilisers – nitrogen, potash and phosphates. Some of these elements are taken up by the crop to give greatly enhanced yields, but some also remains in the soil or, in the case of nitrates, slowly percolates into streams or down into the groundwater, a particular problem in the Leam Valley area. At the other end of the cycle, the large amounts of dung produced by dairy cattle can now be a problem, to be stored or applied to the land as a liquid slurry. This can then all too easily wash into ditches and streams, killing the invertebrate life there.

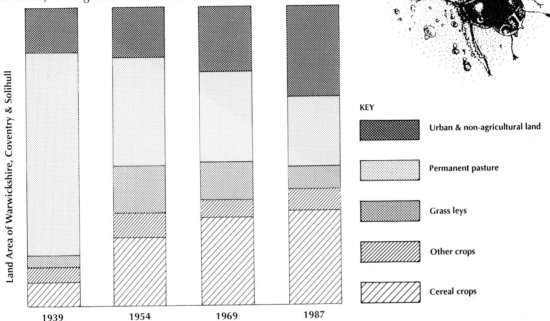

KEY

Urban & non-agricultural land

Permanent pasture

Grass leys

Other crops

Cereal crops

Farming changes in Warwickshire from 1939-1987: the main ones have been an increase in cereals from 8% to over 30% of the land surface, coupled with a decline in total area of farmland as towns have expanded. Permanent pasture has declined from nearly 70% of the county to just 23%. (AT, data courtesy of MAFF)

Even in Warwickshire too much water can be a problem, leading to crop losses when fields are waterlogged, so under-field drainage has been improved since Victorian times. More efficient plastic pipes now underlie most arable land across the county, getting water more quickly off the land but requiring more dredging of streams and rivers to cope with the sudden influx of water after heavy rain. The water also carries topsoil with it, leaching away the very silts and clays so important to soil structure.

As mechanisation developed, it became more economically beneficial to remove hedgerows, creating larger fields from Austrey to Brailes for bigger machinery. These are then sown with a single crop species – and usually with a single variety of the one crop. Hardly surprisingly, a pest or disease can have a tremendous impact on this monoculture system, increasing from one year to the next as the same crop can now be grown year after year. New chemicals then become necessary, not just to control an outbreak of a pest or disease, but to try to prevent it occurring. Further inevitable consequences are the development of resistance to these chemicals among the few survivors, which then breed and pass on their resistance to new

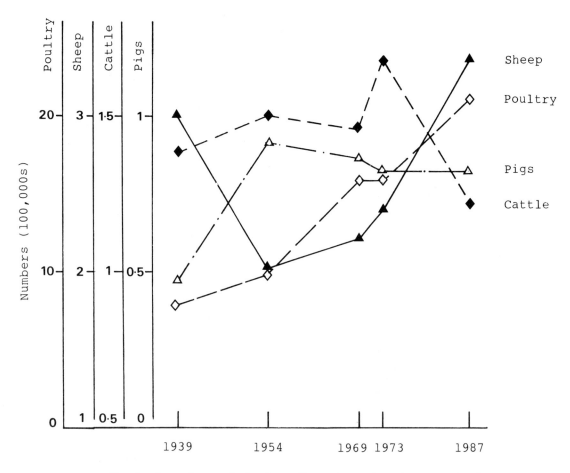

FARM LIVESTOCK CHANGES 1939 - 1987

Despite these changes in land-use, livestock numbers have remained
more constant. (AT, data courtesy of MAFF)

generations. This battle between plant breeders, chemical manufacturers and the biology of the
pest species – animal, plant or fungus – continues to develop in complexity, with farmers
constantly encouraged to keep up with the newest technology.

Other wild flowers of cultivation include fat hen, knotgrass, black bindweed and groundsel,
with colourful flowers of common field speedwell, scarlet pimpernel, and field pansy. Less
common are the fluellens with tiny snapdragon-like flowers and blue pimpernel at Oxhouse
Farm, with trailing St John's wort and field madder on a fruit farm near Kenilworth.

In the days of the wildwood, thousands of years ago, these arable weeds must have been
uncommon species, growing on soil freshly exposed by flooding, by trees blowing over or by
animals burrowing in the soil. As Neolithic agriculture began, so the plants flourished in the
newly created bare soil, increasing in numbers a thousand-fold as more land was cleared for
farming. They remained as common plants until the last thirty years, when better ways of
cleaning crop seeds and new chemicals sealed their fate. Now many have disappeared from
Warwickshire and are facing extinction in Britain. The decline continues today, too: shepherd's
needle – a small white flowered member of the carrot family – was described as frequent in

104

Shepherd's needle is now found at only one site in Warwickshire. (CBH)

the 1971 computer-mapped *Flora of Warwickshire*, yet surveys in 1986 and 1987 by the county's top botanists found it in only one location. In the 1930s it was so common that special riddle plates needed to be fitted to threshing machines in some places to stop the seeds, known as puck-needles, from clogging up the hoppers. A nationwide survey of arable weeds organised by the Botanical Society of the British Isles in 1986/7, showed Warwickshire as a last toe-hold for the corn buttercup, with just seven sightings, including Weston-under-Wetherley and Bishops Tachbrook.

Invertebrates on the farm are generally unwelcome, as they can cause considerable economic damage. Many insects are more or less specific to one crop, such as carrot fly, potato capsid and cabbage root fly. Groups such as aphids and flea beetles contain many species, each dependent on one type of plant. Other more general feeders include the larve of crane-flies, eating the roots of any grasses or cereals, or the pollen beetles, eating flowers. Slugs and snails too are fairly non-specific feeders, spending their lives grazing with a rasp-like radula to scrape off bits of plant tissue. Some species are actually carnivorous, feeding on earthworms, centipedes, and other slugs. In arable land, both the field slug and the keeled slug can do extensive damage to cereal crops and oil-seed rape. Probably the most important group of invertebrates on the farm are the worms, whose constant activity adds to both fertility and drainage.

It is not only arable weeds that are in decline: numbers of grey partridge are going down too because of the changes in arable farming. Here the cause is more complex, but factors such as stubble burning, autumn ploughing, and the increased use of insecticides have all played a part in reducing sawfly larvae, a key part of the diet for young partridges. Other species still seem to thrive, however, with skylark and lapwing foremost as birds of the farm. Skylark nests on the ground among grass or a young crop, and singing in flight it has no need of hedgerows or trees. Although few lapwing breed in the county, their numbers are swollen by migrants from the Baltic, Russia and the uplands of Britain, so that by December flocks may be several thousand strong. So easy to see in flight with their black and white markings, it is always surprising how readily they blend into a ploughed field. Often mixed flocks are formed with

Winter flocks of lapwing may number several thousand, although fewer breed in the county. (MM)

105

other species joining in: golden plover are worth looking out for, together with the inevitable black-headed gulls and starlings. The corn bunting is a bird of tree-less arable fields, whose numbers have increased significantly in Warwickshire over the last forty years. The species has a strong affinity for barley fields and can be seen from Shipston-on-Stour to Austrey. The Avon valley is a favoured location for winter roosts, with a hundred or so in reed-beds from Eathorpe to Brandon. Quail is nowhere common in Warwickshire, but occasionally may be found breeding in both northern and southern extremities of the county.

Arable fields in winter around Monks Kirby, Long Lawford, Grandborough and Welford-on-Avon provide food for other birds too. Wood pigeon are generally unwelcome as they eat young rape crops, feasting on the cabbage-like leaves. Fieldfares and redwings, arriving here from Scandinavia throughout Warwickshire, feed on underground invertebrates such as cranefly larvae ('leather jackets') and earthworms. When the ground freezes, the birds move on to the hedgerow hawthorn and holly berries. Rooks also feed on invertebrates, preferring a mixed farm with scattered copses, as these colonial crows' social lives revolve around a rookery of possibly twenty twig-like nests built high up in the tall trees.

The most widespread mammal in farmland is the rabbit, introduced in the Middle Ages from the warmer Mediterranean region to provide fresh meat throughout the winter. Originally people went to great lengths to maintain local rabbit populations by building warrens for them and even digging burrows! At some stage during the intervening five hundred years rabbits have acclimatised and it seems surprising now that they ever had difficulty in breeding in Britain. By the late eighteenth century the rabbit had become regarded as an agricultural pest and so some welcomed the introduction of the myxomatosis virus in the 1950s, which decimated the population. The few survivors that had resistance to the disease are now breeding successfully, and with each doe producing three to six litters a year, averaging five kittens in each, the rabbit has considerable potential for growth.

The rabbit's native relative, the brown hare, lives entirely above ground, lying by day in a small hollow – the 'form' – from which it comes out at dusk to feed and forage. Although they eat some crops, the amount of damage they do is only small, particularly compared with the damage they can cause to young plantations. In recent years numbers of hares have declined, possibly because of the changes in arable farming already described.

Once widespread throughout most of England, hedges form an integral part of the rural landscape. They arose by accident along boundaries between landholdings, or by design when enclosure hedges were put up to keep in sheep and keep out people. Whether dating back to pre-Roman times or only a hundred years, all hedges have the same function of keeping livestock in defined areas. In order to do this they were traditionally 'layed' or 'layered', a technique that involves cutting the stems of the shrubs or trees nearly – but not quite – all the way through. The stems, now called 'pleachers', can then be laid almost horizontally, and

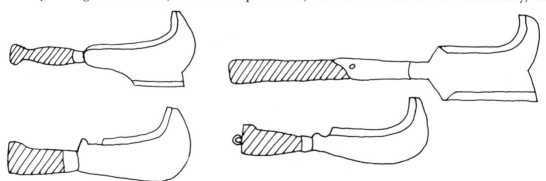

Billhooks from ABOVE: Warwickshire compared to those of Yorkshire and BELOW: the West Country. (CBH after BTCV)

106

woven in and out of upright stakes put in the ground at about half-metre intervals. This procedure is carried out all along the hedge, weaving each next stem over the previous one to give a strong and stock-proof barrier. In Warwickshire it was traditional to top off hedges with a twisted binding of hazel 'featherings' to give a neat appearance. Whole industries grew up in the last century to support the demand for hedging, with different styles of billhook specific to different regions. The double-bladed Warwickshire billhook was favoured in most parts of the Midlands, but long handled Yorkshire billhooks were also used, along with the heavier Staffordshire billhook. Such hedges were relaid every fifteen or twenty years, and cut back by hand in the winter months every few years. Today, with labour costs a major component of farming, the tractor-mounted flail mower is used almost everywhere, chopping through everything in its path, to give neat low hedges. Unfortunately this mechanised process does not easily differentiate between hedge and developing trees, unlike farm labourers working by hand, so there are fewer young hedgerow trees to be found now.

Good laid hedges can still be found, however, along the roadsides at Ullenhall, Hill Wootton, and Southam, and the Trust keeps the tradition alive with training courses and practical help.

Hedges themselves have declined as the reason for their usefulness – keeping in livestock – is no longer valid. Arable crops need no hedges to keep them in, and large machines need big fields. Hedgerow loss in Warwickshire has not been so great as in the east of England, but nevertheless the county has seen significant removals over the last thirty years. Many of them in south-east Warwickshire were relatively recent enclosure hedges, dating back one or two hundred years, but they were often an important strip of habitat for birds, mammals and insects, as well as a corridor for movement in the countryside. Worse in wildlife and cultural terms is the destruction of ancient hedgerow, possibly dating back to the wildwood and certainly many centuries old. These hedges are far more than just barriers to livestock and, with their diversity of tree and shrub species, wild flowers and invertebrates, they are like miniature woodland systems, all with stories to tell. The wild flowers present at the bottom of these ancient hedges at Moreton Morrell and Tile Hill include bluebell, sweet violet and wood anemone – reminders of a woodland past – as well as the graceful foxglove, which flourishes in the hedgebanks of the north (as at Middleton) and west (as at Hockley Heath). Hedges can also provide shelter for grassland plants such as cowslip and knapweed, but most typically the hedge will abut a roadside verge of white umbellifers, with the arching stems of false oat-grass and the red flowers of hedge woundwort or red campion. In some farms the practice of spraying herbicide into the hedge bottom has effectively destroyed all of this beauty, only to replace it when the spraying stops with cleavers, barren brome and couch grass. Fortunately the practice of spraying out hedge bottoms is declining, and the value of hedges themselves in harbouring natural predators of pest species is leading to less destruction.

Farm buildings may seem unlikely habitats for wildlife, yet two different animals benefit. The barn owl is dependent naturally on hollow trees for nesting but has made its home in barns for centuries. It also needs rough grassland to hunt over for its prey of mice and voles. Barn owls are suffering because many barns particularly around Stratford-on-Avon, have been converted to houses and much rough grassland has disappeared, leading to a decline in numbers despite the owl's readiness to breed. Most bats also depend on rough grassland to provide them with the flying insects that they feed on during their night-time hunting. Common bats of farmland include pipistrelle, noctule and brown long-eared, but other species are found too. Bats declined as pesticides reduced the numbers of insects and thus their food supply, but many are showing some signs of recovery now. All are specially protected under the Wildlife and Countryside Act 1981.

Brown long-eared bats are not so common as pipistrelles, but are widespread in the county. (CBH)

Often the best farm habitat for wildlife is the unmanaged land tucked away in an inaccessible corner, surrounding an old pond or marl pit, or along a streamside. These also include spinneys and tree-planted field corners, as well as more substantial small woods. Some, like Trust reserves at Newton Gorse or Decoy Spinney form vital islands of habitat in otherwise open farmland. Such areas, if not tidied up too often, may provide invaluable habitat for a wide range of species, including birds such as yellowhammer, corn bunting, chaffinch, dunnock, blackbird and wren.

A positive sign in farming over recent years has been an increased appreciation of the value of wildlife areas, promoted by the local Farming and Wildlife Advisory Group (FWAG). Organic farming too is making its mark as a serious method of food production. With new potential for non-productive lands and farm diversification, the last ten years of the century could see a resurgence for wildlife on the farm.

OPPOSITE ABOVE: Oil-seed rape has dramatically changed Warwickshire's colour. (FCM)
BELOW: Common poppy flourishes when the ground is disturbed. (RC) CENTRE: Barn owl.
(TH) BELOW: Lapwing are widespread on grasslands and arable fields throughout the county.
(ML) RIGHT: Brown hare have declined over the last ten years. (TH)

ABOVE: Ploughing as it was in 1915: a German prisoner of war leads the horses at Toft Farm near Dunchurch. (Courtesy of JSR) BELOW: Ploughing today: one person ploughs six furrows at once, harrowing the previous furrows at the same time. (JSR)

ABOVE: Drainage of arable land in 1886: the team is ready for work
(JSR) BELOW: Drainage today: most arable and pasture fields are now
underdrained. (JRR)

OPPOSITE LEFT: Barley crop at Dunchurch. (KR) RIGHT: Corn cockle is now extinct in the county. (AT) BELOW: Scarlet pimpernel survives in field corners. (JRR)

OVE: Sheep are on the increase in the county, here at Leek Wootton. ...K) BELOW: An insect dependent on cattle – the dung fly. (JRR)

ABOVE: Hedgerows form important habitats on farms: here the blackthorn is in flower. (JRR) BELOW: A newly laid hedge at Ufton Wood. The Trust now offers a hedge-laying service. (MWF)

114

ABOVE: Hedgerow removal is fortunately not so widespread as ten years ago. (JRR) BELOW: A hedge-less landscape is poor for wildlife, here near the county boundary in the south-east. (AT)

Wildlife in Town

(CBH)

When the fox hath once got in his nose,
He'll soon find means to make his body follow

Henry VI, Part 3

The phrase 'urban wildlife' might have seemed a paradox only a few years ago, as towns and nature do not at first sight go together. However, the growth of dedicated Urban Wildlife Groups across the nation has demonstrated that all towns and cities have areas of value to wildlife, and sometimes areas of exceptional value. Within Warwickshire, the city of Coventry dominates in size and influence, with about a third of a million inhabitants. Solihull is growing rapidly towards a hundred thousand as it spreads out from Birmingham towards the M42 motorway. There are three towns of about sixty thousand people – Nuneaton, Rugby and Leamington Spa, with a further three of about twenty thousand – Kenilworth, Warwick and Stratford-on-Avon. Completing the picture are smaller towns throughout the county from Atherstone and Coleshill in the north, through Bedworth to Alcester and Shipston-on-Stour in the south.

These towns have followed classic patterns of development, many located on rivers, where lines of communication meet and where the land could easily be defended. Later, growth of industry and expansion of housing have spread in waves around the original centres, building over and destroying the natural habitats or surrounding them with buildings. This has given rise to two types of wildlife: those species able to adapt and thrive in the urban environment, and those which survive in the encapsulated countryside preserved as the town has expanded.

Good examples of opportunist species include foxes and starlings among the animals, and buddleia and rosebay willowherb as plant representatives. The urban fox is an excellent symbol of a survivor, an animal able to adapt to a changing environment and indeed turn it to advantage: Shakespeare's words of 400 years ago still ring true today. In the summer of 1988 a survey of foxes, carried out in conjunction with a local radio station, revealed a large number of sightings within extremely urban settings, such as one regularly seen wandering up the steps of Coventry Cathedral in the small hours of the morning. Perhaps the most revealing information was the affection and support that local foxes attracted. Many people were

ABOVE: Fieldfare need hedgerow berries for winter feeding. (WNCT)
LEFT: Foxglove, a hedgerow plant. (JRR) RIGHT: Hedge brown, a
hedgerow butterfly. (CM)

117

regularly feeding them; in Leamington a fox would come along to a garden every evening to play with a cat; in Bedworth classes at a school were happily disrupted by their fox, who came to stare through the window. The intelligence of the fox was also shown by the Coventry animal that was to be seen walking down a road every Tuesday evening, examining the rubbish bags put out for collection next morning. Very much a success story in terms of adapting to the urban way of life, the fox illustrates the tenacity of nature in surviving apparently against all odds.

Urban and suburban gardens with trees and shrubs have some similarities to woodland edge, and many birds of this habitat now thrive in towns. Species such as bluetit, great tit, blackbird and robin are just as common in all the towns of Warwickshire as they are in woodlands. The number of these small songbirds also attracts the attention of predators, such as sparrowhawks and magpies. Just outside a Coventry hospital a sparrowhawk has surprised both patients and

Sparrowhawks often feed on starlings in towns. (TH)

118

Rosebay willowherb thrives on disturbed ground, especially after fires. (CBH)

visitors by its rapid swoop to take its prey. Perhaps the most spectacular sight, however, involves the huge starling population coming to roost in Coventry city centre, and reflecting another species adapting to life in an urban environment. Naturally, starlings roost in woods or on cliffs: our town centres now provide a similar facility, with tall trees and large buildings, and the bonus of temperatures a degree or two warmer. Quite often it is possible to see a sparrowhawk right in the heart of the city, preying on this aerobatic display team.

In winter, large numbers of pied wagtails sometimes gather to roost in factories or secluded courtyards and grey wagtails are occasionally seen in industrial and shopping areas, where they feed in rainwater puddles on flat roofs. Careful searching might reveal an even bigger surprise. Most prized is the black redstart – a recent colonist to Britain, which began to nest on bombed sites and derelict areas during the last war. As a breeding bird, it is now well established in Birmingham, occurs irregularly in Coventry and at Hams Hall power station, and has been recorded at Galley Common, Rugby and Warwick. Favoured sites are power stations, gas works and similarly large industrial plants, especially those near waste ground and water.

The story of the buddleia is ironic, as non-native species which invade a new country usually have deleterious side-effects. However, for the buddleia there seems to be only success. Firstly, it succeeds in growing almost anywhere, from gutters to gaps between paving slabs. Secondly, it provides a much needed resource of nectar for insects and especially butterflies such as peacock, small tortoiseshell and red admiral. Finally, the buddleia supports many aphids, which in turn are eaten by birds or parasitized by ichneumon wasps. All are valuable plusses for wildlife within the city.

Other plants of waste ground have shown astonishing ability to survive under pressure too. The rosebay willowherb has three characters enabling it to do well in towns: it produces masses of wind-borne seed and so increases its chances of getting to a suitable germination site; it thrives on ground burned after a fire; and it can spread vegetatively with underground stolons. With this background it is not surprising that rosebay flourished on Coventry bomb sites in the 1940s and still does well on midlands demolition sites and railway embankments today. In its wake comes the elephant hawk-moth, whose caterpillars feed on rosebay and great willowherb. The caterpillars themselves have two pairs of amazingly detailed eyespot markings at the front of their body, and pull in their head when alarmed, to reveal an apparently large-eyed monster!

Within the urban environment are areas of land with high wildlife value that have been surrounded as the towns have expanded. These may be ancient woodlands such as Tile Hill Wood, Coventry; old meadows like Welche's Meadow, Leamington Spa; commons or river valleys like the Cole Valley, Solihull, but they can still retain much of their wildlife value despite the pressures. Their survival is dependent on sensitive management, based on an appreciation of their wildlife value. It is all too easy in an urban setting to plant conifers in ancient woods because someone has decided they look nice, or to spread fertiliser and spray herbicides on an old hay meadow to get rid of the wild flower 'weeds', or even to put the river into a culvert and pipe it under the town because it looks too untidy and its value for real estate is too high. Fortunately such negative attitudes are now being resisted by more people, but the legacy of past errors is still there for all to see.

Of all the habitats present in towns, probably woodlands have fared the best. Examples of good ancient woodlands within an urban setting include Tile Hill, Willenhall and Tocil Woods in Coventry, and Yorks Wood and Bills Wood in Solihull. Even with woodlands, the situation

119

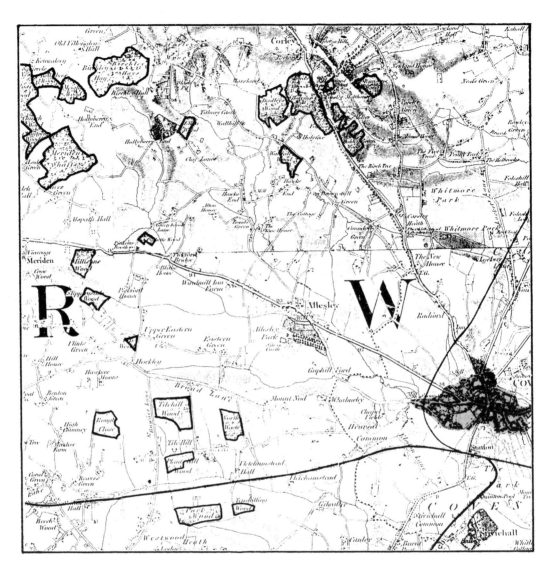

150 Years of urban expansion: ABOVE: Meriden-Corley-Coventry area in the 1830s. The built-up parts of the city are shaded, and woodlands outlined in black.

is not always good, however, as at Chelmsley Wood, where houses and flats have now replaced the trees and wild flowers that used to abound. Meadows in towns are even more vulnerable to damage or destruction, so it is all the more surprising that any survive. Those that do are usually close to rivers or streams, tucked away out of site to developers. Some commons still survive in urban areas, including Hearsall Common in Coventry, part mown grass but part scrub woodland, and home to jays, lizards and a huge population of frogs. Kenilworth Common to the north of the town provides a relict heathland area, as does Grendon Common near Atherstone. A small heathy area also survives at the aptly-named Gorse Valley, Camp Hill, where gorse, wood sage and lady's bedstraw flourish alongside small heath and meadow brown butterflies. Most commons and most heaths have, however, been built on or transformed into urban parks.

120

Meriden-Corley-Coventry at the same scale in the 1980s. Some woods and commons have been engulfed by the expanding city but still remain intact. in contrast, woods south of Corley and Meriden Shafts Wood have been severely reduced, and Slipperyslide Wood south-east of Meriden has disappeared completely. (A: First edition OS map WRO; B: based on 1988 1:50,000 OS map © Crown Copyright)

Rivers, and their artificial counterparts, the canals, provide an important habitat within most urban centres, and also link the countryside around them. The most important is the River Blythe, now designated a Site of Special Scientific Interest, because of the excellent wildlife value of the river and adjacent wet meadows. The Blythe begins life in rural land to the south of Birmingham, passing through Solihull's Brueton Park on its way to join the River Tame at the aptly named Blyth End near Coleshill. Further north at Tamworth it is joined by the River Anker, which forms a valuable green corridor through the towns of Polesworth and Atherstone. Warwickshire's most famous river, the Avon, also brings the countryside into the towns of Rugby, Warwick, Stratford and Bidford, with important tributaries of the Sowe in Coventry and Leam in Leamington Spa. At Rugby it is joined by the River Swift, but somehow the potential for recognising the value of these rivers – and the Oxford Canal – for either wildlife or people has yet to be fulfilled. Riverside grassland alongside the Anker is Nuneaton

121

is much reduced, and meadows along the Finham Brook in Kenilworth are under pressure. However, there are more optimistic signs for fields alongside the Arrow in Alcester, the Avon in Stratford and the Leam in Leamington, where new nature reserves are planned. Welches Meadow in Leamington still floods every winter, providing a valuable winter roost for snipe, although changes to its drainage pattern have altered the balance of the 200 species of wild flowers recorded from the site. Further from the town, the River Leam provides valuable habitats for king fishers and lady's smock as it skirts the Campion Hills at Newbold Comyn.

Kingfishers can also be seen along the River Sherborne as it passes through Coventry's Lake View Park, a large urban park which still contains remnants of old hedgerows. The River Sowe, running through the east of the city, now forms the core of a designated green wedge, valuable open space for people and wildlife alike, with three Local Nature Reserves along its length: Wyken Slough, Stoke Floods, and Stonebridge Meadows. Wyken Slough contains medieval ridge-and-furrow grassland as well as a lake and marsh; Stoke Floods has a valuable subsidence lake alongside the river, with reed-beds and coot, and Stonebridge Meadow has acidic grassland with wet alder woodland. Another excellent site, Henley Road Meadow, is still a managed hay meadow, full of ragged robin, great burnet and meadow buttercup, yet surrounded by suburbs in the north-east of the city.

At Stratford-on-Avon the town and river have been synonymous with swans for centuries, referred to by Shakespeare and part of the town council's coat of arms. In the 1950s the mute swan flock probably numbered a hundred or so, and even in 1964 the flock of about 60 was thought strong enough to allow a dozen birds to be exported to California, USA. However, in the later 1960s and 1970s numbers declined as lead poisoning took its toll. The lead – mostly from discarded fishing weights – had been taken in as the swans fed and, ground up with gravel in their gizzards, it was absorbed into their blood stream. The story was also further complicated by the possibility of boats churning up the river bed to expose more lead, and by changes in the river vegetation. The good news, however, is that, with the phasing out of lead weights, swans have now returned to Stratford. A special Swan Reserve has been established, and the Avon valley should once again see the spectacle of swans flying up and down in safety.

Canals in urban areas are often treated as tips, but they too are important for wildlife, not just as corridors for movement. Kingfishers can be seen flying along Coventry Canal in one of the city's most industrial areas at Longford. The canal is, in fact, rich in wildlife, with freshwater crayfish and great-crested newts among its animals and flowering rush, yellow flag and gipsywort along the waterside. The canal also travels through Bedworth, Nuneaton and Atherstone, bringing dragonflies and damselflies to these towns. The Grand Union Canal links Warwick and Leamington with the surrounding countryside, and then passes through Solihull on its way to Birmingham, another vital aquatic link for boats and wildlife alike. Both the Stratford Canal and the Oxford Canal are well-used for pleasure boating, but they too have many good wildlife habitats along their length.

Links over land are provided by roads and railways, both of which reach right into the centre of towns from the surrounding countryside. The verges, embankments and cuttings along these routes provide important urban habitats of grassland, scrub and woodland, sometimes sufficiently valuable to become nature reserves, as at the disused railway at Ashlawn in Rugby. Here the 150-year-old cutting passes through lime-rich soils, encouraging both common spotted and green veined

Common frogs now depend on urban ponds for their survival. (CBH)

122

orchids, as well as common blue and marbled white butterflies. North of the town the same line has cowslips and common fleabane at Newton. Grasslands are home to many small mammals such as voles, mice and shrews, which attract two particular predators. The urban fox has already been described but its avian equivalent, the kestrel, can be seen throughout the county, hovering over roadside verges or grassy embankments, a symbol of the natural health of such areas. In this respect motorways have had a positive impact on Warwickshire, providing many acres of rough grassland where previously arable farmland predominated. The impact of the new roads on existing habitats has also been much more closely studied than in previous times, even to the extent of mapping badger setts and paths along the route of the M40, so that tunnels can be provided to separate badgers from cars, to the better health of both.

Industry's impact on the environment of towns and countryside alike has been enormous. Most of this has been negative, but some positive consequences include quarrying for limestone, which has created habitats for grassland species. Digging for sand and gravel has resulted in lakes and wetlands, and mining subsidence from the coal industry has created various shallow pools throughout the north of the county. Coal-mining has also left a legacy of spoil heaps – waste materials mined from the ground and then left in huge tips. This spoil material is usually acid, due to the mineral pyrite naturally present in the clays and shales, and it is often highly desirable to reclaim such tips for beneficial use. However, when left to develop naturally, such unpromising beginnings can produce gems in wildlife terms. Many old abandoned tips in north Warwickshire now contain heathland vegetation with gorses and wavy hair-grass, as at Baxterley and Dordon. Where drainage is impeded, valuable marshes can also develop. The best of these in the county is Herald Way on the eastern edge of Coventry, scheduled as a Site of Special Scientific Interest in 1989 because of the rare insects occurring here. A total of 433 species have been recorded, including two classed as nationally vulnerable and five nationally 'notable'. There is conflict here unfortunately because, despite the site's designation, its mass of southern marsh orchid hybrids, its glow worms and its breeding reed and sedge warblers, the land is also scheduled for building development and its future looks bleak.

In Warwick, the land where Emscote Power Station was demolished also contains colliery spoil, but the surprising wildlife interest centres on sand, imported from the coast of south Wales over thirty years ago to extinguish a deep-seated fire. Also imported to Warwick were the sand-dune species of plants and insects, which began to flourish. Early colonisers such as sand couch and sand catstail have since gone, but marram grass and sand sedge are still there, along with the colourful restharrow, viper's bugloss and evening primrose. This site too is under threat from development. In Rugby the huge quarries, on which much of the town's

Small tortoiseshell butterflies feed on many nectar-bearing flowers, including creeping thistle. Their caterpillars depend entirely on nettles, and can often be found in school and garden wildlife areas. (HC)

prosperity was based, contain areas with masses of beautiful lime-loving wild flowers such as bird's foot – trefoil, centaury and common spotted orchid. Here it is hoped that sympathetic management will encourage them to flourish.

Within the towns two additional habitats for wildlife remain: parks and gardens. Traditionally managed parks, with ornamental flower beds, close-mown grass and sports pitches, clearly have little value for wildlife and indeed, this is the intention. However, across the country, local authorities are realising that not all of every park needs to be maintained like this. In nearly every park there is scope for wild areas to be created, whether wildlife ponds, hay meadows, or spinneys. Such areas can be cheap to maintain while providing an additional source of pleasure to park users. Some parks already have a head start, with mature trees and shrubs providing nesting and feeding habitats for species such as nuthatches, treecreepers and even great spotted woodpecker. Some contain uncommon species, such as the autumn crocus in Priory Park, Warwick. A few have actually been designed with wildlife in mind, like Whittleford Park, Nuneaton, with its created habitats of woodland and meadows bringing a natural appearance to the west of the town.

In a similar way to parks, both churchyards and school grounds can benefit from wildlife areas created within them. Over thirty primary schools in Warwickshire as well as many more in Solihull and Coventry already have such facilities right on their doorstep for instant access during lessons. These new wildlife areas are not meant as replacements for lost habitats, but do serve to bring the enjoyment and appreciation of nature to more people, whether adult or child.

Gardens on new housing estates often look open because of their lack of trees. Visit a housing estate thirty or forty years old, however, and the picture is different. Milverton in Leamington Spa provides both side by side. Trees are just as important in the urban landscape as they are in the country, and it is equally important for wildlife that native species are selected rather than exotics or conifers. In the garden, many people already take an interest in wildlife by feeding the birds in winter, but it is surprising how many people then unintentionally harm those same birds in the spring by spraying garden flowers with insecticides. This spraying kills off greenfly and caterpillars, but also deprives the nestlings of blue tits, great tits, wrens and robins of a vital food source. Hedgehogs often thrive in gardens, eating slugs, snails and worms, and they can be further encouraged by putting out food for them: ideally dog or cat food, rather than bread and milk. Slug pellets in the garden can spell disaster for hedgehogs as well as the intended slugs. Gardens can be improved for wildlife by creating new wildlife habitats: digging a pond, making a mini-meadow or simply planting native shrubs, such as one of the buckthorns, to encourage brimstone butterflies. With the right habitats, gardens are becoming more important for a wide range of species, the common frog now depending more on ponds in gardens than farm ponds. Even houses themselves can play a part, the angled eaves on gable ends resembling cliff faces for nest-building house martins, and any crack serving as an entry hole for roosting bats – especially the tiny pipistrelle. Gardens are also important as part of a network of open spaces throughout the urban area, linking in with other gardens and wildlife corridors to the surrounding countryside. With wildlife everywhere under pressure, there is no doubt that urban wildlife must be here to stay.

Hedgehogs can be encouraged in gardens by providing food from autumn onwards, so they build up weight before hibernation. (CBH)

The tiny pipistrelle bat can be seen at dusk in many suburban gardens as it hunts for insects. (CBH)

ABOVE: Chelmsley Wood was an ancient woodland: now it is a housing estate and suburb of Birmingham. (JRR) BELOW: Stoke Floods nature reserve on the banks of the River Sowe in Coventry is surrounded by housing, yet provides an important wetland habitat. (AT)

ABOVE: Welche's Meadow in Leamington Spa is an old flood meadow on the banks of the River Leam, soon to become a local nature reserve. (JRR) BELOW: Herald Way Marsh SSSI in Coventry is threatened with warehouse development. (CM)

126

LEFT: Southern marsh orchids hybridise at Herald Way Marsh. (JRR) RIGHT: Railways provide valuable wildlife corridors through urban areas, here at Willenhall, Coventry. (AT) BELOW: Disused railway lines can be even more important for wildlife, as at Ashlawn Cutting nature reserve in Rugby. (JRR)

RIGHT: Even in the built-up areas there are still important green spaces for wildlife, as in Sutton Coldfield. (NMW) ABOVE: Southern hawker dragonfly can thrive on city waterways. (FCM) BELOW: Red admiral show the importance of buddleia for quick feeding. (RC) CENTRE: Kestrels have expanded their range and now fly over new road verges along the M42 and M6. (RC)

128

ABOVE: Canals also link town with countryside, as at Coventry Canal. (CMT) BELOW: Urban churchyards sometimes have wildlife areas. (JRR)

ABOVE LEFT: Elephant hawkmoth caterpillars thrive on rosebay willowherb. (JRR) ABOVE RIGHT: The bright yellow flowers of coltsfoot herald spring upon waste ground. (CM) CENTRE LEFT: Peppered moth, a classic example of natural selection, here in its two forms. (AT) RIGHT: Garden spider. (RA) BELOW: Frogs thrive in garden ponds. (FCM)

ABOVE: Foxes are urban survivors. (FCM) LEFT: Grey squirrel have successfully invaded towns and gardens. (FCM) RIGHT: Mute swans can breed successfully in towns, especially at Stratford-on-Avon. (CM)

132

The Way Ahead

(CBH)

One touch of nature makes the whole world kin.

Troilus and Cressida

If the previous chapters have served to show the diversity and beauty of nature in Warwickshire, then the purpose of this final one is to show how vulnerable that wildlife is. 'One touch of nature' may be all it takes, but we need to welcome that touch, not cast it aside.

We now know that the ancient woodlands that have survived are much more than collections of trees. They date back further than any of our cathedrals and castles; their beauty is more natural than any painting or photograph; they are irreplaceable. Yet, because of our ignorance, we continue to abuse them. We cut them down, and in their place plant alien conifers. We isolate them more and more. And we even dig them up to build on the land. How can we expect the tropical rainforest to be protected by its peoples when we fail to protect our own forest?

Our old meadows, on ridge-and-furrow fields or alongside our rivers, are liberally coated with fertilisers to improve their yields, and sprayed with herbicides to kill off the wildflowers. The butterflies go too, as well as the bats that needed the insects for food. So we produce more food, for an economy that says we have too much. But once extinct there is no going back: it is no good saying 'sorry'.

Heathlands are so fragile that nearly all are already gone. Few fragments remain but even here they are still seen as waste land, unwanted and unproductive, prime candidates for tipping and building. Farewell to both heather and lizards.

Wetland marshes and field ponds are often looked upon simply as unproductive land to be filled in for 'agricultural improvement' or for building houses or warehouses. Larger holes in the ground are commercially valuable: tipping can produce a greater return than digging out the hole in the first place, so it makes economic sense to bulldoze that marsh, that quarry, those newts, dragonflies, and reed warblers. How do we keep the kingfishers or herons if they have nowhere to fish?

Many individual species have also disappeared from the county over the last hundred years: fritillary were once found in Warwickshire's wet meadows: purple emperor butterflies flew in Brandon Wood; sand lizards now rare in Britain once lived near Alcester, and the song of the corncrake was heard around Stratford-on-Avon. To these four examples could be added many others, species lost as habitats have been destroyed.

LEFT: This wren has taken over an old swallow nest. (RC) CENTRE: Spotted flycatchers are a welcome urban visitor. (FCM) RIGHT: Blue tits can be encouraged by nest boxes. BELOW: Use of garden pesticides will kill off birds' food too. (AGM)

133

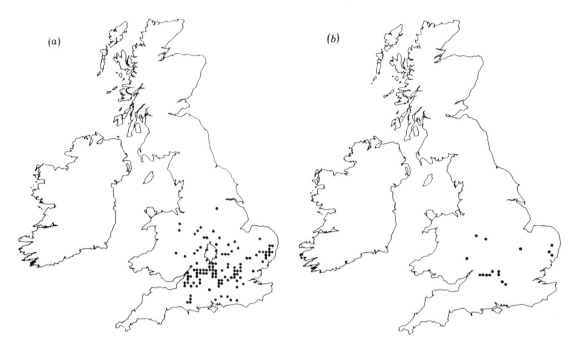

(a)

(b)

The distribution of the fritillary in Britain – A: before 1930; B: in 1970.
The plant is now extinct in Warwickshire as its habitat of unimproved wet
meadows has disappeared. (from *Changes in our native vascular plant flora* by
Perring (1974) with kind permission of Classey)

We have shown, in Warwickshire, that people can conquer nature entirely. We can chop it down, dig it up, build on it. What we have yet to show conclusively is that we have the will to live with it, enjoying and valuing nature for what it is, not just for an economic return. Only when we can all look around the county, in our towns and in our countryside, and see a picture of people and nature living side by side, can we really claim to be a caring county.

Over twenty years ago some people did care enough about the threats facing our natural environment to do something about it, and so Warwickshire Nature Conservation Trust was founded in 1970, as a registered charity aiming to protect and conserve wildlife and natural habitats throughout Warwickshire, Coventry and Solihull. Since those early days the Trust has grown considerably, thanks to increasing support from people everywhere. The Trust is also part of a national network of 48 Wildlife Trusts, all partners in RSNC – the Royal Society for Nature Conservation.

Many of the best woodlands in the county are now protected as Trust Nature Reserves. Some are owned by the Trust, including Clowes Wood, Lion Wood, Ryton Wood, Old Nun Wood, Snitterfield Bushes and Hampton Wood. Others are managed by agreement with the owners, from Newton Gorse through Temple Balsall and Tocil Wood to Hanging Wood.

The Trust also owns some of the county's top grasslands, from Deans Green Meadows and Shadowbrook Meadows to the incomparable Draycote Meadows. Other grassland is managed by agreement at Priory Fields, Stonebridge Meadows, Ufton Fields and Oxhouse Farm. Still further grassland sites in old railway cuttings are also owned by the Trust: Henley Sidings, Harbury Spoilbank, and Goldicote Cutting, with Ashlawn Cutting managed under a lease.

In wetlands too the Trust has made an impact, owning over 100 acres of land in the Tame valley at Whitacre Heath, leasing a further 70 acres at Alvecote Pools and licensing 175 acres in the Avon valley at Brandon Marsh. Smaller wetland reserves at Wyken Slough, Stoke Floods and Eathorpe complete this wetland picture.

The Trust now manages nearly 40 nature reserves, scattered all over Warwickshire, Coventry and Solihull, and covering over 2,000 acres. Purchase of land has only been possible through many grants and donations, with legacies playing a key part. Where Nature Reserve Agreements have been arranged with landowners, this is due to their sympathetic approach and caring attitude.

The Government's conservation advisors, the Nature Conservancy Council (NCC), have also been active in helping to protect the top key sites, known as Sites of Special Scientific Interest (SSSIs). This designation has been given to many Trust Reserves as well as to privately owned land, and is intended to protect the natural importance of the site from adverse impact. NCC has also declared many geological SSSIs, so protecting the geological importance of these sites. Other bodies too have nature reserves in the county, including the West Midlands Bird Club reserve at Ladywalk, the County Council's reserve in Kingsbury Water Park, reserves at Hams Hall power station, at the Springfield Centre, and the Woodland Trust reserve of Piles Coppice.

However, all these nature reserves and SSSIs on their own can only protect a small percentage of Warwickshire's wildlife. What happens to wildlife in the rest of the county is mainly up to the attitudes of the land's owners, as legal protection is only patchy, with some species protected (such as great crested newts, bats, badgers and some birds) but all too often their habitat– vital for their survival – not protected at all.

One way to conserve the natural features of the county is to ensure that they are protected by the planning system. Many local authorities across England have now completed surveys of their natural habitats, so that they know what is there. Many have gone further, developing strategies and policies to ensure that they keep a place for nature as developments occur. Councillors have approved these moves, not only because there are votes to be won, but also because towns and country can genuinely be better to live in if there is space for nature too.

Many people now enjoy watching wildlife: more will need to show their support if it is to have a future in Warwickshire. (TH)

135

Although none of our local authorities in Warwickshire has yet produced such a nature conservation strategy, some are making encouraging steps along this path. Some too are realising the value of informal green spaces in towns, with the Green Track network in Nuneaton, the Sowe Valley project in Coventry, and the Great Central Walkway in Rugby.

Farmers have a key part to play in conserving the nature of Warwickshire, and many farms now have their own wildlife area, new spinneys or lakes. Set-aside areas and headlands also give new habitats for wildlife to flourish in. Businesses too have begun to realise that they have to put some resources back into nature, and are sponsoring a wide range of Trust activities and projects as well as improving their local working environment for wildlife. Some developments have actually been designed to take nature into account, and add additional habitats to new housing estates, supermarkets, or business parks. As yet these are only small steps, but they are in the right direction, and must be encouraged. Landscaping of new developments also offers many opportunities to use native trees, shrubs and wild flowers in order to create new habitats for wildlife, not just planting for cosmetic colours.

The other positive sign is that more people than ever before are now aware of the environment, and their individual powers to do something about it. More people are joining the Trust, with nearly 5,000 members now expressing their commitment to our Warwickshire wildlife. More people are getting involved, helping with both time and money to ensure that there are places for nature where they live. Put together this represents a big investment of time and energy in caring for our environment.

The Trust itself is also doing more for wildlife than it ever has before, with new projects and initiatives to promote nature conservation throughout the county. In order to generate more income to support its work, the Trust has set up shops and sells logs from its woodlands. More recently it has begun selling its trading services as consultants, landscape contractors and providers of training. These additional activities allow more people to work to protect Warwickshire wildlife, and spread the message of conservation. New groups have been set up, to encourage more people to get involved: the Bat Group, Badger Group, Geology Group and Urban Wildlife Group all give new opportunities for action, alongside the traditional practical conservation volunteering.

For Warwickshire more than most counties, the future for wildlife lies in the hands of the people. We have created the towns and the countryside: we can also make a space for wildlife if we wish.

Logos of RSNC, WATCH, Trust and trading company.

ABOVE: Pond clearance at Stoke Floods nature reserve. (MST)
BELOW: Building a raised bird hide at Brandon Marsh nature reserve.
(CM)

ABOVE: Conservation volunteers at Ryton Wood nature reserve. (SP) LEFT: Helping toads across the roads. (JWL) RIGHT: Making hay on Dean's Green nature reserve using the Trust's sponsored hay-making equipment. (ACW)

ABOVE: Tree planting can add valuable habitats. (CET) BELOW: Getting enthused about wildlife with David Bellamy at Binley Woods school. (CET)

Finding out about wildlife with WATCH. (CET)

Appendix: Trust Nature Reserves and Other Places of Wildlife Interest

ALVECOTE POOLS SSSI *Trust Reserve, 3km E of Tamworth*
A series of shallow lakes formed by mining subsidence, with many breeding birds and passage migrants as well as unusual wetland plants.

ASHLAWN CUTTING *Trust Reserve, SE Rugby*
Steep-sided disused railway cutting through lime-rich clays, giving many chalk-grassland wild flowers and butterflies including common blue and green hairstreak.

BISHOPS BOWL *Reserve Agreement, Bishops Itchington*
Old limestone quarry now a commercial fishery. Excellent views of Lower Lias rocks and nature trail to lime-rich grassland and butterflies.

BRANDON MARSH SSSI *Trust Reserve, 2km SE of Coventry*
Pools and marshes from sand and gravel extraction, now naturally colonised and managed to encourage birds. Wetlands with grassland and woodland too: 5 bird hides.

BRANDON WOOD *Forestry Commission, S Binley Woods*
Forestry Commission wood on ancient woodland site, now managed for amenity with local group. Good ground flora, insects, and breeding birds.

BURTON DASSETT *Country Park (WCC), 3km W of Fenny Compton*
Old grassland on ironstone cappings to Dassett Hills offering good views of south Warwickshire. Grasslands with interesting wild flowers.

CARPSWELL POOL *Trust Reserve, 2km N of Shrewley*
Old fishpond supporting tufted duck and surrounded by a variety of trees. A small meadow area has meadow brown butterflies in abundance.

CLOWES WOOD SSSI *Trust Reserve, 1km W of Earlswood*
Broadleaved woodland on acid soils, with areas of heathy vegetation and a wet meadow. Excellent for fungi in the autumn: the woodland flora in spring includes lily-of-the-valley.

COOMBE ABBEY SSSI *Country Park (CCC), 3km E of Coventry*
Buildings and estate, including lakes, meadows, park and woodland. Good heronry by lake and excellent diversity of bats around the buildings and water.

DEANS GREEN *Trust Reserve, 3km NE of Henley*
Two old meadows, one regularly mown as a hay meadow, the other being reinstated. Plants include betony, saw-wort and adder's tongue fern.

DECOY SPINNEY *Trust Reserve, 0.5km S of Stareton*
Old overgrown duck decoy surrounded by mixed woodland. Conifers are being slowly replaced with broadleaved trees: wood is part of a farm walk at Stoneleigh.

DRAYCOTE MEADOWS SSSI *Trust Reserve, 0.5km N of Draycote*
Two species-rich hay meadows, with many wild flowers typical of old unimproved grassland: green-veined orchids in abundance in late May.

DRAYCOTE WATER *Country Park (WCC), 3km SW of Dunchurch*
The large reservoir is extensively used for sailing, windsurfing and fishing, but has excellent bird list. Adjacent Country Park provides additional greenspace.

EARLSWOOD MOATHOUSE *Trust Reserve, 1km S of Earlswood*
Oak woodland on acid soils with two adjacent meadows planted in 1980 with native trees and shrubs to encourage birds. Two ponds also present.

EATHORPE *trust Reserve, 0.5km SW of Eathorpe*
Small area of marshland next to River Leam. Good insect, aquatic and bird life on what is only a small area of land.

ELMDON MANOR *Trust Reserve, 0.5km SW of Elmdon*
Old walled garden with meadow, woodland and ponds. Planned development as wildflower nursery, with additional nature trail.

GOLDICOTE CUTTING *Trust Reserve, 4km SE of Stratford*
800m of disused railway cutting through Lower Lias clays, with chalk grassland flora. Dry banks support a population of lizards.

HAMPTON WOOD *Trust Reserve, 1.5km SW of Barford*
Ancient woodland, partly grazed in the past, with newly-reinstated coppice. Adjacent meadow and stream lead to River Avon. Primroses notable in the spring.

HAMS HALL *CEBG Reserve, 4km N of Coleshill*
Nature reserve developed by the CEGB on a power station site, part of the Tame valley complex. A range of habitats for educational use.

HANGING WOOD *Trust Reserve, 1km W of Claverdon*
Ancient woodland with small-leaved lime and wild service tree. Coppice regime with oak standards, and excellent bluebells in the spring.

HARBURY SPOILBANK SSSI *Trust Reserve, 1km E of Harbury*
Lime-rich grassland and scrub on old spoil material from adjacent railway cutting. Marbled white and green hairstreak butterflies, fieldfare in winter.

HARTSHILL HAYES *Country Park, NW Hartshill*
Ancient woodland with planted conifers but remnants of small-leaved lime and oaks. Adjacent grassland and open spaces provide excellent habitats.

HAY WOOD *Forestry Commission, 2km N of Rowington*
Site of ancient woodland but now planted with conifers, there are still open rides and glades with spring flowers and ferns.

HENLEY SIDINGS *Trust Reserve, 0.5km N of Henley*
500m length of railway cutting with characteristic flora of lime-rich soil and cowslips in the spring.

KINGSBURY WATER PARK *Country Park (WCC), 2km W of Kingsbury*
Extensive area of old sand and gravel quarries, now lakes. Used for sailing and recreation, but with nature reserve area excellent for birds.

LADYWALK *WMBC Reserve, 2km SW of Whitacre Heath*
West Midland Bird Club reserve in the Tame valley complex of pools and lakes, with excellent records of migrant birds.

LION WOOD *Trust Reserve, 0.5km S of Portway*
Small oak woodland with heather and bilberry on acid soil. Ridge-and-furrow evident. Jointly owned with Worcestershire Trust.

NEWTON GORSE *Trust Reserve, 0.5km N of Newton Regis*
Small mixed woodland in an open part of the county. Good for typical woodland birds such as warblers and tits as well as sparrowhawk.

OLD NUN WOOD *Trust Reserve, 2km W of Princethorpe*
Small oak/hazel woodland in the Ryton/Wappenbury/Princethorpe complex. Woodland wild flowers and breeding birds are typical of surrounding woods.

OXHOUSE FARM SSSI *Trust Reserve, 2km SW of Combrook*
Traditional farm, privately owned, and managed for wildlife. Good hay meadows and scrub woodland with a beautiful section of the River Dene.

PILES COPPICE *Woodland Trust, 2km SE of Coventry*
Ancient small-leaved lime and sessile oak woodland, with ancient woodland earthworks and ground flora including yellow archangel.

PINLEY ABBEY SPINNEYS *Trust Reserve, 1km NE of Claverdon*
Two small spinneys and a hay meadow. Ponds in the wood and rough grassland areas are maintained specifically to encourage bird life.

PRIORY FIELDS *Trust Reserve, Yardley Wood*
Marshy grassland bounded by Stratford-on-Avon canal. Mixture of acid and lime-loving plants, as well as small area of tree-planting.

RYTON POOL *Picnic Site (WCC), 2km SE of Ryton*
Pools remaining from quarrying with restored vegetation and nature trail around margins. Great crested grebe on lake.

RYTON WOOD SSSI *Trust Reserve, 2km S of Ryton*
Ancient woodland with oak, hazel and small-leaved lime. Bracken glades and wet rides with uncommon flowers: excellent woodland birds and butterflies.

SNITTERFIELD BUSHES SSSI *Trust Reserve, 1km W of Snitterfield*
Semi-natural woodland, much affected by wartime airfield. Ash/oak woodland on limey clays, with early purple orchid, herb paris and wayfaring tree.

SHADOWBROOK MEADOWS *Trust Reserve, 1.5km W of Hampton in Arden*
Series of four old meadows with stream and wooded area. Common spotted orchids, betony and marsh marigold with other hay meadow wild flowers.

SPRINGFIELD CENTRE *Birmingham CC, 3km E of Knowle*
Environmental studies centre, adjacent to Temple Balsall Nature Reserve. Specific facilities for disabled access and enjoyment of wildlife.

STOCKTON CUTTING SSSI *Trust Reserve, 1km N of Stockton*
Steep sided disused railway cutting through Lias limestones, with adjacent pool and developing woodland. Excellent habitat for migrating birds.

STOKE FLOODS *Trust Reserve, E Coventry*
Lake adjacent to River Sowe, surrounded by reedbeds and by housing, yet retaining its importance to birds.

STONEBRIDGE MEADOWS *Trust Reserve, S Coventry*
Unimproved pasture on banks of River Sowe, including wet alder woodland and dry acid grassland with harebell and tormentil.

TEMPLE BALSALL *Trust Reserve, 3km E of Knowle*
Damp woodland with marsh, pond and stream. Butterbur, snowdrop and yellow flag. Adjacent to Springfield Environmental Centre.

THE ISLAND TYSOE *Trust Reserve, SW Upper Tysoe*
Small area of damp woodland and meadow alongside a stream in a fairly open part of the county. Cowslips in the grassland and spindle tree present.

TOCIL WOOD *Trust Reserve, University of Warwick*
Remnant of ancient woodland now surrounded by the University. Hazel coppicing reinstated and sycamore cleared in wood: additional meadow at rear.

UFTON FIELDS SSSI *Trust Reserve, 0.5km S of Ufton*
Disused quarry for whire Lias limestone with pools, developing woodland, and open grassland. Five orchid species, small blues and green woodpecker.

WAPPENBURY WOOD *FC/Trust Reserve, 2km E of Bubbenhall*
Ancient woodland site owned by Forestry Commission. Good for woodland plants, insects and birds, especially in rides and clearings.

WHITACRE HEATH SSSI *Trust Reserve, 1km W of Whitacre Heath*
Old gravel workings on the banks of the River Tame, with reed beds and willow carr. Bird hide overlooks new scrape: excellent birds on passage.

WYKEN SLOUGH *Trust Reserve, NE Coventry*
Marsh to the north of Wyken Pool is good for snipe: other habitats in the area include the lake itself, meadows and hedgerows.

For details of access to any of these sites, please contact the appropriate organisation:
WARWICKSHIRE NATURE CONSERVATION TRUST
    Montague Road, Warwick CV34 5LW
WARWICKSHIRE COUNTY COUNCIL
    Planning Department, Shire Hall, Warwick CV34 4SX
COVENTRY CITY COUNCIL
    Countryside Unit, Dept of Planning, Tower Block, Much Park Street, Coventry CV1 2PY
FORESTRY COMMISSION
    Midlands District Office, Rugeley, Staffordshire WS15 2UQ
THE WOODLAND TRUST
    Autumn Park, Dysart Road, Grantham, Lincolnshire NG31 6LL
HAMS HALL ENVIRONMENTAL CENTRE
    Hams Hall Power Station, Lea Marston, Sutton Coldfield B76 0BG
SPRINGFIELD ENVIRONMENTAL CENTRE
    Kenilworth Road, Knowle, Solihull B93 0AJ
WEST MIDLAND BIRD CLUB
    Membership Secretary, 296 Olton Boulevard West, Birmingham B11 3HH

Please enclose a stamped addressed envelope with your letter.

Further Reading

1. Warwickshire

CADBURY, D.A., HAWKES, J.G. & READETT, R.C. (1971) *A Computer-Mapped Flora; A Study of the County of Warwickshire.* Birmingham Natural History Society/Academic Press, London
CLARK, M.C. (1980) *A Fungus Flora of Warwickshire* Birmingham Natural History Society/British Mycological Society, London
COPSON, P.J. (1986) *Windows on Warwickshire* Warwickshire Museum Service, Warwick
DIX, H.M. & HUGHES, D.R. (1960) *The Coventry District; A Naturalist's Guide* Coventry and District Natural History and Scientific Society, Coventry
HARRISON, G.R., DEAN, A.R., RICHARDS, A.J. & SMALLSHIRE, D. (1982) *The Birds of the West Midlands* West Midland Bird Club, Studley

2. General

BAINES, C. (1985) *How to Make a Wildlife Garden* Elm Tree Books, London
BAKER, A.R.H. & BUTLIN, R.A. (Eds.) (1973) *Studies of the Field Systems in the British Isles* University Press, Cambridge
BECKETT, K. & BECKETT, G. (1979) *Planting Native Trees and Shrubs* Jarold, Norwich
CORBET, G.B. & SOUTHERN, H.N. (Eds.) (1964) *The Handbook of British Mammals* Mammal Society/Blackwell, Oxford
EMERY, M. (1986) *Promoting Nature in Towns and Cities A Practical Guide* Croom Helm, London.
HILL, F. (1988) *Wildlife Gardening – a Practical Handbook* Derbyshire Wildlife Trust, Derby
HYWELL-DAVIES, J. & THOM, V. (Eds.) (1984) *The Macmillan Guide to Britain's Nature Reserves* RSNC/Macmillan, London
MABEY, R. & EVANS, T. (1980) *The Flowering of Britain* Arrow, London
MORRIS, P. (Ed.) (1979) *The Country Life Book of the Natural History of the British Isles* Country Life Books, Richmond-on-Thames
PAGE, C.N. (1982) *The Ferns of Britain and Ireland* University Press, Cambridge
PERRING, F.H. & WALTERS, S.M. (1962) *Atlas of the British Flora* BSBI/Thomas Nelson, London
PETERKEN, G.F. (1981) *Woodland Conservation and Management* Chapman & Hall, London
RACKHAM, O. (1986) *The History of the Countryside* Dent, London
RATCLIFFE, D. (1977) *A Nature Conservation Review* (2 volumes) University Press, Cambridge
ROBERTSON, J. (1990) *The Complete Bat* Chatto & Windus, London
SHARROCK, J.T.R. (1976) *The Atlas of Breeding Birds in Britain and Ireland* BTO/A&D Poyser, Stafford

3. Identification Books

There are very many books to help with the identification of plants and animals: this selection should help both beginners and those with some experience.

BROOKS, M. & KNIGHT, C. (1982) *A Complete Guide to the British Butterflies* Cape, London
CHINNERY, M. (1986) *Collins Guide to the Insects of Britain and Western Europe* Collins, London
FITTER, R., FITTER, A. & FARRER, A. (1984) *Collins Guide to the Grasses, Sedges, Rushes and Ferns of Britain and Northern Europe* Collins, London
HAYMAN, P. (1979) *The Mitchell Beazley Birdwatcher's Pocket Guide* RSPB/Mitchell Beazley, London
LYNEBORG, L. (1971) *Mammals in Colour* Blandford, Poole
MITCHELL, A. (1974) *A Field Guide to the Trees of Britain and Northern Europe* Collins, London
ROSE, F. (1981) *The Wild Flower Key* Warne, London

Further information, together with details of local Natural History Societies, can be obtained from the Biological Records Centres at the Warwickshire Museum, Market Place, Warwick, CV34 4SA and the Herbert Art Gallery and Museum, Jordan Well, Coventry, CV1 5RW, as well as from Warwickshire Nature Conservation Trust, Montague Road, Warwick, CV34 5LW. To contact Nature Conservancy Council (NCC) please write to: 10 Butchers Row, Banbury, OX16 8JH for the County of Warwickshire or Attingham Park, Shrewsbury SY4 4TW for Coventry and Solihull.

Index

146

148

Moorhen. (CBH)

Subscribers

Presentation Copies

1   **The Warwickshire Nature Conservation Trust**
2   **The Royal Society for Nature Conservation**
3   **The Nature Conservancy Council**
4   **Warwickshire County Library**
6   **Coventry City Council**
7   **Solihull Metropolitan Borough Council**
8   **Sir David Attenborough**

9 Dr Andy Tasker
10 George & Maurice Arnold
11 Juliet Bailey
12 Joe Hardman
13 Graham Harrison
14 David Morfitt
15 John Roberts
16 Prof Fred Shotton
17 Roger Smith
18 Chris Thomas
19 Adam Wright
20 Colin Marsay
21 Chris Brookes-Harris
22 Clive & Carolyn Birch
23 David N. Robinson
24 Neil M. Wyatt
25 Craig William Emms
26 Richard Denver Lord
27 John R. Duffy
28 A.W. Brand
29 D.C. Lindsay
30 W.G. Adams
31 A.C.D. McColm
32 Geraint M. Lewis
33 William Wilson DL
34 Nigel A.H. Bailey
35 A.W. Bates
36 H.F. Hopkins
37 Julie Unitt
38 Mrs D.A. Mayo
39 W.T. Hall
40 J.M. Sharpe
41 Francis Hatfield
42 Fern Hodges
43 Joe & Ann Hardman
44 Mr & Mrs J Hodge
45 Peter Hunter
46 Mrs G.E. Scott
47 Claire Fowler-Sutton
48 Christopher Latham
49 Alan Baker
50 Joyce F. Strachan
51 M.A. Arnold
52 Keith Stokes
53 S.E. Bowkett
54 A. Lewis
55 R.N. Robinson
56 Thelma Lea
57 M.A. Truelove
58 Michael Hunter Rowe
59 Bob Crowther
60 Margaret King

61 E.M. Hughes
62 James Victor Branston
63 E.M. Phipps
64
65 G.A. Arnold
66 A.E. Lord
67 S.G. Derrick
68 John Walton
69 Mr & Mrs R.E. Day
70 Angela French
71 B.D. Cooper
72 R.E. Bennett
73 David Honey
74 Patricia Paul
75 B.G. Turton
76 D. Oldham
77 Fern Hodges
78 Paul Norman
79 N.W. & S.M. Hurd
80 John B. Hoyle
81
82 Brian R. Mitchell
83 M.J. Carter
84 Elizabeth Ann Taylor
85 S.M. Apted
86 David Porter
87 Mrs Beryl Haskins
88 Michael R. Jakeman
89 Dr D.J. Gobbett
90 Lorna A. Watson
91 G.N.F. Browning
92 Richard Blight
93 John Wilkin
94 Merle Ann Mason
95 G.H. Green
96 Philip A. Pain
97 Stephanie M. Spiers
98 Dr Peter M. Christopher
99 Carolyn Howard
100 Rev & Mrs D. Ching
101 Christopher Voss
102 Margaret J. Priest
103 Patricia Streather
104 Mrs Anne

    Richardson
105 R.J. Wheway
106 Dilys J. Went
107 M.J. Brice
108 Mrs Margaret M. Pontifex
109 Dr D.J. Jeffray
110 M.G. Carpenter
111
112 M.H. Moor
113 J. Gabryliszyn
114 David Woodcock
115 Teresa M. Castelino
116 S. Tyrrell
117 Peter Charles Rolfe
118 Ann M. Parker
119 Susan Hallett
120 Michael Barrie
121 Graham E. Marriott
122 W.A. Rogers
123 Mrs D. Dorning
124 D.W. Hildred
125 Richard W. Watkins
126 Humphrey Smith
127 Mrs P.M. Bishop
128 Alan Millward
129 Gillian Thornton
130 Andrew F.J. Gardner
131
132 Leony Albrecht Brown
133 Bill & Joyce Steel
134 M.E. Wilson Smith
135 Westwood Library University of Warwick
136
137 Dr & Mrs D.C.C. Wurr
138 Mark Clive Singlehurst
139 Margaret E. Riley
140 K.A. Gaunt
141 M.F. Helsby
142 J. Wood
143 Tom Mooney
144 Steve Valentine
145
146 C.A. Harley
147 H.A. Hill

148 Mrs Prudence Morris
149 Birmingham City Council
150 Miss K.L. Southall
151 G.D. Braithwaite
152 H.A. Roberts
153 Steve Haynes
154 Michael J. Nixon
155 J.W. Garratt
156 Brian Webster
157 L.E. Moore
158 The Warwickshire Museum
159 K. Binks
160 Pamela Copson
161 Roger Christopher Feasy
162 Mrs C. Lea
163 Victor Leslie Miles
164 Philip Godding
165 John Patrick
166 The Library of Warwick School
167 The Hopkins Family
168 Marie Brooke-Harris
169 Patrick Ann Buckley
170 John & Margaret Way
171 S.A. Taylor
172 Dorothy Parry
173 Janet Andrews
174 M. Van Garderen
175 Celia Rickers
176 Sally & John Stringer
177 Miss A.M. Dunn
178 W.C. Keen
179 John H. Barker
180 Valerie Justice
181 Cliff Carnell
182 P.A. Jeavons
183 J.D.W. Field
184 Bill Adams
185 Miss Shirley Watkins
186 W.D. Douthwaite
187 David Marland
188 J.J. Randall
189 W.D. Steele
190 M.D. Hancock
191 Mrs B.E. Clewlow
192 R.H. Graham Suggett
193 Mrs M. Wilkinson
194 Albert Stanley
195 M.I. Gunn

196	Madge Sheehan	257	Harold H. Fowkes
197	John Edward Fox	258	Dorothy J. Herlihy
198	Arthur Pollard	259	S.M. Wilkinson
199	Dionne L.	260	Chryss Davies
	Sambrook	261	Malcolm & Russ
200	David Gash		Welch
201	Mrs D.G.S.	262	Peter Davies
	Thompson	263	A.T. Atkins
202		264	D. & S. Errington
203	G.J.D. Martin	265	Mrs J. Wellan
204	Mrs E.P. Gardener	266	Ronald E. Parr
205	Keith N.A.	267	Margaret A.
	Alexander		Baldock
206	Mrs Ann Beeny	268	Mrs W.R.H.
207	Mrs P. Brazier		Marsden
208	Phyllis & Peter	269	Colin James Box
	Puddifoot	270	Rodney Morris
209	S.B. Butler	271	A. Baston
210	Dr F.M. Slater	272	Francesca Hanikova
211	Dr & Mrs E.V.L.	273	E. & C.J. Jackson
	Hughes	274	J.A. Knights
212	Martin Smith	275	M.G. & S.M.
213	Rachel Berger		Woodhams
214	Mr & Mrs Keith	276	Miss Julie M.
	J.J. Grierson		Wilson
215	Gerry Taylor	277	Sue Holmes
216	J. Shellard	278	Mrs Mary Briggs
217	Henley School	279	Ronald Gulliford
	Conservation	280	Margaret G.
	Group		Massey
218	Solihull Public	281	J. Gould
227	Libraries	282	John W. Roberts
228	Frank & Tabby	283	Dr W.T. Jackson
	Lucas	284	'Coventry's'
229	P.B. Hides	285	Mrs Jennifer M.
230	P.M. Rowberry		Meir
231	G.J. & P.A. Jeffrey	286	Robert Dewbery
232	Mid-Warwickshire	287	Central Library,
	College of	296	Solihull
	Further Education	297	Carolyn Voss
233		298	John Lampitt
234	Mrs S.M. Price	299	Dr R.S. Greenwood
235	Gwen Proudlock	300	Mr & Mrs E.
236	Catherine Lee		Souter
	McArthur	301	Mr & Mrs W.J.
237	Adrian Waller		Dunn
238	Jean Carter	302	Martin Sands
239	David Smith	303	A.G. Wellum
240	R.E. Haycock	304	Jane Cooke
241	Mrs J.M. Duffy	305	Margaret M. Kirk
242	A.D. Smith	306	D.G. Parker
243	J.N. Diserens	307	Mrs Julie Ward
244	Mrs Doreen Neal	308	A.G. Shankster
245	E.T. Wilmot	309	K. Iggulden
246	Maureen Killeby	310	Norman W. Bayliss
247	B.R. Flavell	311	D.I. Langstone
248	Lorna Dudley	312	David Couchman
249	C. Willcox	313	D.E. Sollis
250	Phillip Porter	314	Leslie H. Pinkness
251	J.M. Attwater	315	Mrs J. Tomlins
252	H.E. Wells	316	H.W. Eccles
253	Michael John Slater	317	Derek M. Walton
254	Margaret Cutforth	318	Mrs M.M.C. Harris
255	A.V. Clewes	319	E.G. Scriven
256	John R. Roberts	320	T.R. & J.M. Brock

321	Brian Seaton	376	Nicholas Hobday
322	Mrs Dawn Egging	377	Ann-Rosemary
323	Mrs Rosemary K.F.		Harris
	Clarke	378	C.R. Jefferson
324	J.P. Russell	379	Jim Russell
325	John Perkins	380	Ray Allen
326	Edwin A. Hopkins	381	Martin Popplewell
327		382	Jean Payne
	R. Whittenbury	383	David Barnes
328		384	Charles Hamilton
329	Dr Christine M.	385	D.J. Roberts
	West	386	Peter F. Holloway
330	Brian Tasker	387	Barrie J. Noble
331	S.R. Crathorne	388	Martin Noble
332	E.A. Stransky	389	
333	Richard Meredith		James S. Ross
334	Ruth Moffatt	390	
335	Colin Harris	391	W. Hayston
336	C.N. Gardner	392	L.J. Wright
337	Stephen Farmery	393	Diane Boardman
338	Geoffrey Taylor	394	J.M. Stansbie
339	Shirley Oakley	395	G.R. Stratford
340	Angela Blakeway	396	Michael Burns &
341	Maureen Byrne		Karen Thomas
342	John Richard	397	A. Newton
	Bolton	398	Frank Pearson
343	Pete & Gill Harris	399	Jan Watts
344	Irene & Roy Harris	400	Gillian Plaskett
345	Paul W. Holley	401	H.W. Noar
346	Joan & Len	402	Ron Hill
	Matthews	403	Chris Duke
347	Stephen Farmery	404	Lynn Richardson
348	Geoffrey Taylor	405	R.V.J. Cadbury
349	Shirley Oakley	406	A.J. Redding
350	Angela Blakeway	407	Roy Canning
351	Maureen Byrne	408	Rachel Ann
352	John Richard		England
	Bolton	409	Jill Taylor
353	F.G. Stokes	410	King Henry VIII
354	Georgina Russell		School, Coventry
355	N. Tribe	411	Mary Harrison
356	Mrs P.J. Richardson	412	A.W. Morris
357	Rosemary Ann	413	Janet Arthurton
	Bignell	414	Hazel Lyons
358	Exhall Grange	415	Joyce Barkla
	School	416	Dr David van Rest
359	Joan McGill	417	Helen N. Gardner
360	Aubrey C. Nicholls	418	Mary Comber
361	Mrs J.A. Price	419	Emily King
362	Mrs Germaine	420	Alan Williams
	Ballinger	421	Pauline Hornby
363	Ms Ann Lucas	422	George Yates
364	Alison Glaisher	423	Margaret Vickery
365	Ruth Glaisher	424	R.A. Waller
366	Paul Rendall	425	Robert Ingram
367	P. Speddings	426	A.W.H. Wincott
368	Gerald Ashbury	427	S.J. Benneworth
369	George Webb	428	Marjorie Yates
370	J.A. Bryant	429	Christopher Ivin
371	Mr & Mrs C.M.	430	George Jones
	Bell	431	
372	Helen Nelson	432	Colin Marsay
373	Anthony E.	433	Nichola Jane
	Richards	434	Rossiter
374	Roger Kendrick	435	Joyce Shelley
375	Edward John Hall		

436 Mrs Margaret Thorne
437 Eric Barnes
438 Melody Goddard
439 Rev T.T. Rutherford
440 Mr & Mrs D. Mason
441 Stephanie Long & Kevin Forsyth
442 Deena Blundell
443 John A. Jackson
444 J.F. Watts
445 G.T. Woodin
446 T.B. Hutton
447 Jon Holmes
448 Michael James Morgan
449 I.A.P. Woolford
450 Dr Joan Ashley
451 P.L. Cordle
452 Dr Marshall Wilson
453 David B. Bragg
454 Monica Hazel Sparks
455 S.J. Benneworth
456 M.E. Thomas
457 Audrey L. Clarke
458 Kathleen Hanks
459 Eileen & Rodney Knight
460 F.R. Johnston
461 P.V. Capper
462 Gladys Cooper
463 S. Armstead
464 David A. Marland
465 H. Pluyaar
466 Alan Van Loon
467 Robert A. Arculus
468 Mrs M.C. Finch

469 W.H. Sutton
470 N.L. Thomas
471 Stella Jarman
472 Stephanie E. Armstrong
473 Audrée & Douglas Dunbar
474 Gwen & Geoffrey Dunbar
475 Barbara Davies
476 Adrian Darby
477 Colin Grinnell
478 Robin Orphan
479 G.P. Wheeler
480 S.M. Harris
481 Majorie E. Clarke
482 Audrey Hooker
483 Mr & Mrs B. Noon
484 Brian Clive Holt
485 Mary Hunt
486 Mrs D. Quirke
487 Birmingham Public Libraries
488 Marion M. Green
489 Joyce Martin
490 Heather I. Goss
491 Warwick Junior School
492 Janet Vendore
494 Janet Vendore
495 Mr & Mrs Roy Langford
496 Nick Eborall
497 Leanne Edwards
498 C.E. Bird
499 David N. Roe
500 Dr Jennifer Ann Bent
501 Galen Smith

502 Keith Johnson
503 Edward T. Jury
504 Mrs J. Kingham
505 Richard Storey
506 Jane Moore
507 Warwickshire College of Agriculture
508 Dr J.M. Holmes
509 Department of Leisure & Arts Library Service
510 Stephen Nixpo
511 Brian & Jean Cockayne
512 Mrs J. Russell
513 Michael W. Woodgate
514 Shirley A. Rogers
515 Warwickshire County Record Office
516 Gus Ariss
517 A.D. Wood
518 Michael F. Oakes
519 W.H. Fern
520 Nichola Tayton
521 G.D. Harrison
522 R.I. Jones
523 Sylvia Youngjohns
524 Robert J. Steele
525 Thomas Leslie Twigger
526 Colin J. Mason
527 N. & A. Macfarlane
528 D.W. Cox
529 Warwick Library
530 Roderic J. Darke
531 P. Long

532 Margaret Christine Finch
533 A. Gunton
534 Trevor Trueman
535 P.M. Latcham
536 Miss H. Joyce Opwell
537 H.J. Brennan
538 S.J. Benneworth
539 Karen Gascoigne
540 Peter Smith
541 Marie-Anne Martin
542 Barry Henry Packer
543 Patrick G. Swann
544 Michael Read
545 David R. Shackley
546 Richard Cassley
547 Jim Russell
548 Doreen Langstone
549 D.C. Edwards
550 Dave Champion
551 Alan G. Griffin
552 W.T. Moodie
553 Max J. Harben
554 W.M. Ogden
555 Mrs M.J. Hessey
556 P.W. Stubbs
557 Peter & Fiona Riley
558 David Gathercole
559 Jenny Young
560 Karen Rossiter
561 K.P. Dudley
562 Mrs Rita Smith
563 Mrs E. Broady
564 W.J. Proctor
565 Central Library, Coventry
566
567 Warwickshire
575 County Library

Remaining names unlisted

ENDPAPERS – LEFT: The physical structure of Warwickshire, including Coventry and Solihull. Shaded areas are over 120m (400 feet). (AT/ML redrawn and modified from *A Computer Mapped Flora* edited by Cadbury, 1987). RIGHT: Nature Reserves and Country Parks in Warwickshire, Coventry and Solihull. (CBH)

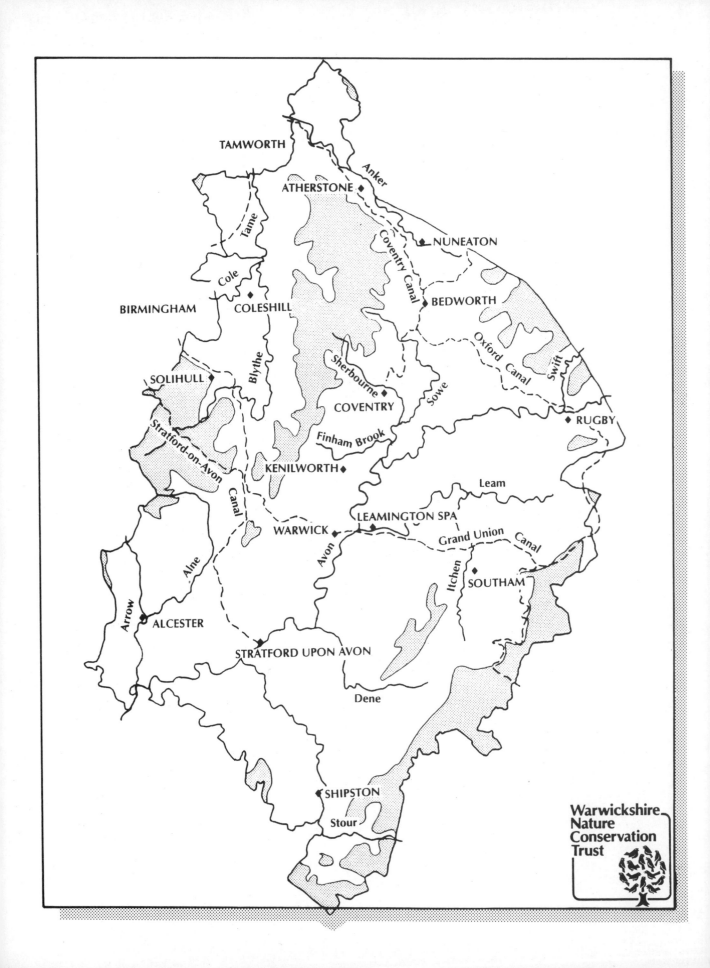

TAMWORTH

ATHERSTONE

Anker

NUNEATON

Coventry Canal

BEDWORTH

Tame

Cole

BIRMINGHAM

COLESHILL

Oxford Canal

Swift

Blythe

Sherbourne

SOLIHULL

COVENTRY

Sowe

RUGBY

Stratford-on-Avon

Finham Brook

KENILWORTH

Leam

Canal

WARWICK

LEAMINGTON SPA

Grand Union Canal

Alne

Avon

Itchen

SOUTHAM

Arrow

ALCESTER

STRATFORD UPON AVON

Dene

SHIPSTON

Stour

Warwickshire Nature Conservation Trust